THE PICTORIAL ENCYCLOPEDIA OF PLANTS AND FLOWERS

The Pictorial Encyclopedia of
PLANTS and FLOWERS

F. A. NOVAK
EDITED BY J. G. BARTON
American Consultant: H. W. Rickett

PAUL HAMLYN · LONDON
CROWN PUBLISHERS, INC., NEW YORK

Designed and produced by Artia.

Published by
The Hamlyn Publishing Group Limited
London · New York · Sydney · Toronto
Hamlyn House, Feltham, Middlesex, England

Published 1966 in Great Britain by Paul Hamlyn Limited
and in the U.S.A. by Crown Publishers, Inc.

Copyright © 1965, 1966 Artia
Translation Copyright © 1965, 1966
Artia and Paul Hamlyn Limited
Reprinted 1967, 1970, 1972

ISBN 0 600 03079 2

Library of Congress Catalog
Card Number: 66-18549
Printed in Czechoslovakia

INTRODUCTION

To many people a plant is a living organism which is rooted in the ground and has green leaves and, perhaps, flowers. While it is true that at the present time the flowering plants occupy a dominant place in the vegetation covering most of the earth's land surface, and also constitute the majority of forms cultivated in farm and garden, a glance through the first hundred pages of this book shows that the plant kingdom has a far greater range.

One of our first problems is to define the terms 'plant' and 'plant kingdom' and distinguish them from 'animal' and 'animal kingdom'. This might seem an easy matter, for the difference between, say, an oak tree and an elephant in mobility, growth, structure, nutrition and reproduction are obvious. However, particularly at the microscopic level, the distinction is not clear and a number of organisms do not readily fit into either kingdom as they are usually defined. Two examples will be given to illustrate this point, concerned with mobility and nutrition. Movement, not involving growth, is a characteristic of most animals, yet there are some which do not move throughout their lives; conversely, there are many bacteria and aquatic algae which, relative to their size, are highly mobile.

Photosynthesis is a fundamental plant characteristic. It is a complex process resulting in the formation of organic compounds from water and carbon dioxide when the green chlorophyll pigments present in the plant are exposed to light. It occurs particularly in the leaves of higher plants, but photosynthetic pigments are found even in the unicellular motile algae. The latter could therefore just as well be considered photosynthetic animals as motile plants! Further confusion arises when it is found that there are forms, closely related to the motile photosynthetic organisms, some of which contain chlorophyll and are non-motile and others which are motile but colourless.

In fact, at this level of organization the two kingdoms merge and the organisms involved are considered primitive, representing ancestral forms from which the main evolutionary lines of the living world have probably originated.

The plant world is divided into several large groups which, as in this book, are often arranged in some sort of linear order. They represent ascending levels of elaboration in structure and organization from the bacteria to the flowering plants. However, it must be emphasized that this is not an evolutionary series, and it is most unlikely that one group gave rise to the one immediately next to it; although what evidence we do have indicates that the less complex forms appeared earlier in the history of life on earth than the more complex.

Including both the unicellular and branched filamentous types there are about 2000 species of bacteria. Their cells are minute, barely visible with an ordinary microscope and they do not possess discrete nuclei, the bodies containing the chromosomes that carry genetic information, which are found in the cells of most other plants. Multiplication by simple cell division is often very rapid and there is little evidence of the type of sexual reproduction which occurs in higher groups. Bacteria are mostly non-photosynthetic and therefore rely on an external supply of organic food material. Hence they live either as saprophytes on the dead remains, or as parasites on the living bodies of other organisms.

The fungi likewise are unable to photosynthesize and the importance of these two groups in the economy of nature is very great. Of particular significance are their saprophytic activities in breaking down dead organic matter and thus maintaining the circulation of the important elements carbon and nitrogen. There are about 50,000 species of fungi and they range from minute unicellular aquatic species to large terrestrial bracket fungi. They produce spores of various kinds which are often dispersed by the wind. Spore output may be enormous and a single average-sized mushroom can produce 1,800 million spores.

There are some 20,000 species of algae including those associated with fungi in lichens. They range from the unicellular primitive forms mentioned above to large seaweeds over 100 feet long. The majority are aquatic and form a large part of the vegetation of seas and lakes. They all contain chlorophylls but these green pigments are often masked by others. In fact colour, allied with other characters, is the basis of the separation of the algae into a number of classes which are not closely related and have probably evolved from different unicellular ancestors. Both asexual and sexual reproduction occur in the algae and in some groups an alternation of generations is found. In this, one generation (sporophyte) produces spores which give rise to another generation (gametophyte). The gametophyte produces sexual gametes and when two of these fuse (often a motile male sperm with a non-motile female egg) the resultant cell develops into another sporophyte. This type of life-cycle is significant as it is the basis of that found in the other major plant groups.

The bryophytes, which include about 25,000 species of liverworts and mosses, are considered an evolutionary side-line. They are small plants with an alternation of generations. The photosynthetic plant is the gametophyte and the sporophyte is a single, usually stalked, capsule which is attached to and more or less dependent upon the gametophyte. Unlike those of the algae the sex organs are surrounded by a layer of sterile cells but external water is still necessary for the sperms to swim to the egg.

The plants so far surveyed are thallophytes and are to be distinguished from the rest of the plant kingdom, the tracheophytes, in that they do not possess vascular tissue. The latter consists of food-conducting phloem and water-conducting xylem which often form a complex, continuous system of strands throughout the plant body. Vascular tissue is characteristic of the land plant as it must have an efficient water transport system to supply the exposed aerial parts. Secondary growth, involving the continuous addition of more xylem to the root and shoot systems, has resulted in the evolution of large tree forms. However, not all vascular plants are large, and a number which have become secondarily aquatic have a very reduced vascular system.

The lower groups of vascular plants, the Psilopsida, Sphenopsida and Lycopsida, reproduce by means of spores which give rise to small, short-lived, non-vascular gametophytes. There are about 1000 living species in these three groups taken together and they are mostly weaker herbaceous plants, but the fossil record indicates that they have had a long history and that in the Carboniferous period some 300 million years ago related forms constituted most of the large forests covering the earth's land surface.

The ferns, too, produce spores and have also existed on earth at least since the Carboniferous period. Owing to the absence of secondary growth, they have never reached the dimensions of forest trees but, in spite of this, they show a considerable range of habit and there are in existence today some 10,000 species. Like the other spore-bearing plants they require external water for fertilization to occur, and in older classification they were put with them in the pteridophytes. Today it is recognized that they have more affinity with the seed-plants, the gymnosperms and angiosperms, and are frequently included with them in the Pteropsida. Support for this view comes from Carboniferous rocks in which fossil, fern-like, seed-bearing foliage is commonly found.

The gymnosperms, like the other group of vascular plants mentioned above, have had a long evolutionary history. They are all trees or shrubs, mostly evergreen, and the exposed seeds are usually borne on cones. Pollination is by wind, and the nutritive tissue in which the embryo is embedded develops from the female gametophyte. At the present time the group includes about 650 species of conifers, richly branched trees with small leaves, and some 100 species of cycads which have thick, generally unbranched trunks and a crown of large, pinnate leaves.

The illustrations in the rest of this book are of flowering plants or angiosperms. The ovules which develop into seeds after pollination and fertilization are completely enclosed in an ovary. The fruit wall which develops from that of the ovary either opens to release the mature seeds or is shed with the seeds inside. The male and female reproductive structures are frequently borne in a single flower but a number of species have unisexual flowers.

Two distinct groups are recognized in the flowering plants, the dicotyledons and the monocotyledons. The former is larger and includes nearly all the trees as well as many shrubs and herbs. Characteristically the embryo in the seed has two seed-leaves or cotyledons, the leaves are often broad and net-veined and the floral parts are in fours or fives. Generally the monocotyledons are herbaceous although the palms and some bamboos attain the stature of trees. Typically the seed embryo has only one cotyledon, the leaves are often narrow with parallel veins, and the floral parts are in threes.

The origin of the flowering plants remains a mystery although several theories have been put forward. It is believed that they existed in the Palaeozoic era but their rapid expansion did not begin until the Mesozoic. Today they form the dominant part of the land vegetation of the earth. There are at least 200,000 species and they range in form from minute plants about ⅛ inch across to enormous trees 250 feet high. Diversity of floral structure is also great and it has been suggested that the rise of the angiosperms is linked to that of insects. Indeed, many intriguing adaptations ensuring insect-pollination are found in the flowering plants, but it must be pointed out that some of the most successful families, e.g. the grasses, are wind-pollinated.

After this brief survey of the plant kingdom, its importance in nature and to man must be emphasized. Animals cannot photosynthesize and therefore are ultimately dependent upon plants for a supply of organic food materials. Numerous food chains can be observed both in the sea and on land and although the intermediate links may involve the carnivorous habit, the beginning always involves the consumption of plant material. The breakdown of organic material by saprophytes in the soil is of prime importance, and the parasites also play an important part in the complex inter-relationship of the living world. In spite of the activities of the modern chemist, man is still to a large extent dependent on the plant kingdom for food, shelter and clothing, and many economically important plants are illustrated in this book. Commercial timbers are obtained from a large number of temperate and tropical trees, softwoods mostly from conifers such as pine, spruce and cedar and the hardwoods from various flowering plant species including the oaks, elms and maples. Most of our food comes from the fruits, seeds or underground storage organs of flowering plants. Of prime importance here is the grass family: rice, corn, wheat, rye and barley are all grasses and they have been intensively cultivated for their grain since earliest times. Furthermore, the grasses constitute large areas of pasture and therefore the meat industry is also largely dependent upon them. Succulent fruits, apples, plums, bananas, tomatoes, olives and many others, and also underground structures such as sweet potatoes, carrots and beets, provide an important part of our diet and some are invaluable for the mineral salts and vitamins they contain. Plants also provide us with fibres such as cotton, sisal and hemp, and are the source of many valuable oils, scents, drugs and dyes. Finally, although not essential for man's existence, we must not forget the ornamental value of plants. The world would be very drab without them.

With the enormous increase in population, and the spread of civilization, wild plants no longer supply sufficient materials for man's needs. Large areas of the earth's surface have been put under cultivation and are specially planted with forests, pasture or food crops. With this activity has developed selection and breeding so that today many of our cultivated plants are very unlike the wild species from which they developed. Sometimes the delicate balance of nature is upset and they become subject to epidemics of animal and fungal diseases. Man is therefore dependent not only upon the plants themselves but also on the forester, farmer, plant breeder and pathologist whose continual efforts are required to ensure that supply does not fall short of demand.

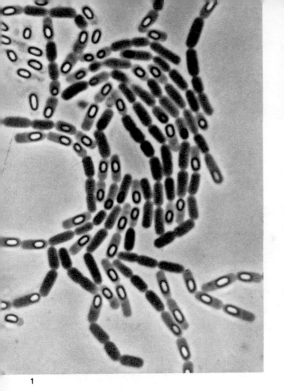

1

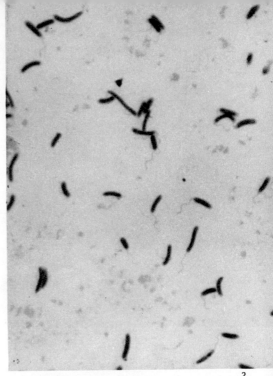

2

3

The **Bacteria** (*Bacteriophyta* or *Schizomycetes*) [1–7] are mostly colourless, one-celled organisms. They are extremely small and little detail can be seen with the oridinary light microscope without special staining techniques. The organization of the cell appears to be somewhat different from that of other organisms. Basically it consists of a wall, cytoplasm and a chromatinic body which corresponds to the nucleus of other plant cells. Division is by binary fission and a portion of the chromatinic body is included in each daughter cell thus formed.

Multiplication is rapid and may result in the formation of chains of cells. Most bacteria have spherical cells (cocci), e.g. *Micrococcus luteus* [6] but some are rod-shaped (bacilli), e.g. *Bacillus subtilis* [5]. A few have curved rods (vibrios), as in *Vibrio cholerae* [2] and a fourth form is found with a spirally twisted cell (spirillum). Many bacteria are motile and are able to swim by the lashing movements of very fine flagella. There may be a single flagellum at one end [2] or a number distributed over the whole surface of the cell as in *Proteus mirabilis* [3]. Some species, for example *Bacillus anthracoides* [1], are capable of forming thick-walled endospores. These are able to resist extreme conditions of heat, cold and dryness and can germinate when exposed to more favourable conditions.

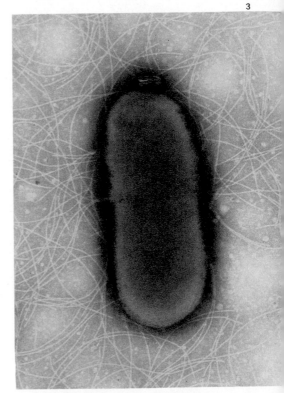

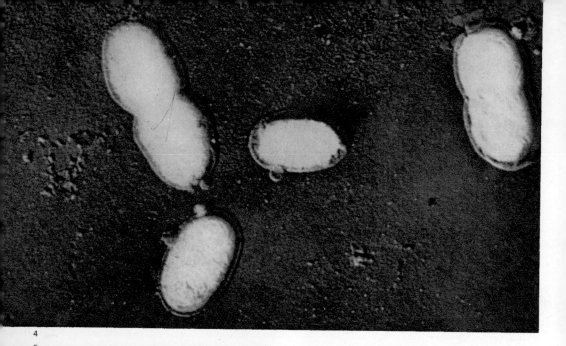

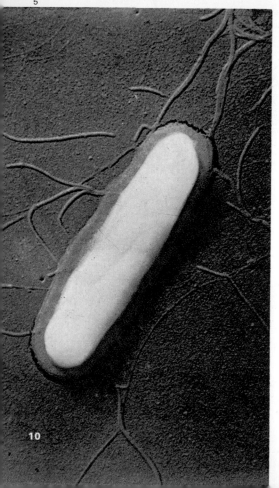

Most bacteria require a source of organic food material and they are abundant in the soil as saprophytes where they play a vital role in the economy of nature. By breaking down the dead remains of animals and plants they release valuable nutrients into the soil and carbon dioxide into the atmosphere. *B. subtilis* [5] is a common soil saprophyte. Other species are parasites of living organisms and some of these are responsible for serious diseases in human beings. *Vibrio cholerae* [2] is the cause of cholera. *Escherichia coli* [4] is normally an intestinal saprophyte but under certain conditions it can become parasitic. It is this bacterium which has been used for research into fundamental genetical problems in recent years.

The identification and classification of bacteria present difficulties owing to the few structural features which can readily be seen. Size, shape and grouping of the cells are used together with number and position of flagella, but recourse is also made to their physiological and biochemical characteristics. These are studied in pure culture and involve their behaviour on special test media.

Much information has been obtained in recent years by the rise of the electron microscope with which photographs [3] to [7] were obtained. Some idea of the size of bacteria can be gained from the magnification of *Bacillus subtilis* [5], which is × 40,000, and of *Proteus vulgaris* [7], × 23,000.

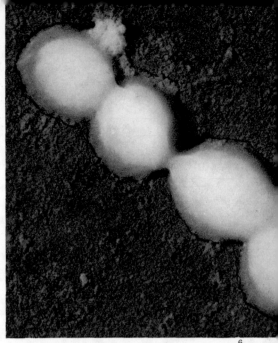

At a somewhat higher level of organization are the **Actinomycetes**, *Actinomycetales*. Most are terrestrial and are like fungi in that they produce fine, branched threads, e.g. *Actinomyces griseus* [8]. They are also like the fungi in that they reproduce by asexual conidia although the cells composing the filaments are about the width of a bacterial cell. Some actinomycetes are the cause of diseases in plants, animals and man; they also have important uses in that some species produce the powerful antibiotics streptomycin and aureomycin.

6

7

8

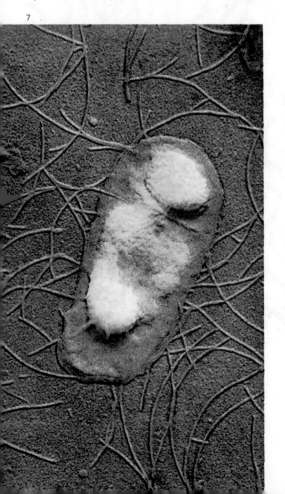

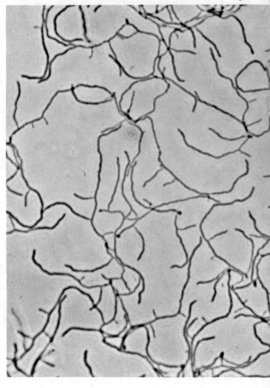

11

9

The **Algae** include a vast range of plants from microscopic, unicellular plants to giant seaweeds more than 100 feet long. Most are aquatic but many are terrestrial or live on damp rocks. They do not possess the woody water-conducting tissue present in vascular plants, but may show considerable complexity in structure and life cycle. They contain green chlorophyll pigments and are therefore capable of photosynthesis,

but other pigments are often present, and the primary classification of the algae is based on colour.

The **Blue-green Algae**, *Cyanophyta* [9, 10], stand rather apart from the other groups in that the organization of the cells is quite like that of bacteria. They grow in water or soil and may be unicellular, colonial or, as in *Nostoc commune* [9], composed of long filaments. Some species are constituents of lichens (p. 45). The filaments of some species have a limited power of movement but they do not possess flagella. As in the bacteria there is no clearly defined nucleus, but the cytoplasm is divided into an inner and outer zone with most of the pigment in the latter. Several pigments are present and the colour varies from pale bluish-green to purple. The filaments usually have a gelatinous sheath which in some forms is so extensive that it forms a common envelope enclosing a large number of filaments. *Aphanizomenon flos-aquae* [10] is one of the planktonic forms which floats just beneath the surface of lakes. At certain times it multiplies so rapidly that the water becomes coloured with the green 'bloom'.

11

The class *Chrysophyta* [11–19] includes a large number of small algae with yellow or golden-brown pigments. They occur in both fresh water and the sea, and form an important part of the plankton. Many are unicellular motile forms with flagella, but colonial and filamentous kinds also occur. The production of internal cysts is a distinctive feature of this group. The genus *Mallomonas* [11–15] is widely distributed in plankton. This is a unicellular form with two lateral pigmented bodies and a large nucleus. The cell is more or less ovoid and possesses a single flagellum which propels it by lashing movements.

12

13

The wall has a number of overlapping silicified scales, e.g. in *M. schwemmlei* [11], some or all of which bear long, needle-like projections. The intricate sculpturing of this complex wall shows up well in the electron micrographs of *M. zellensis* [12], *M. hetero-* *spina* [13], *M. schwemmlei* [14] and *M. paludosa* [15]. A related genus, *Chromulina*, has a similar cell structure with a single apical flagellum, but the complicated rigid wall is absent and the cells can change shape. Other forms have two flagella and calcareous walls.

14

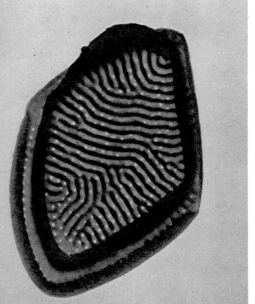

15

15

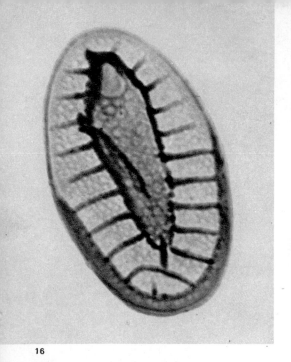

16

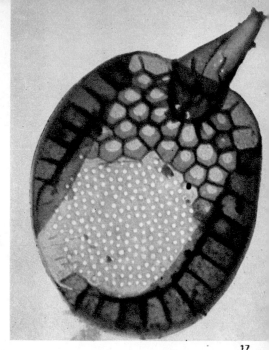

17

The cells in some species of the *Chrysophyta* form branched colonies but in the majority the colonies are more or less spherical. In *Synura* [16–19] the cells are pear-shaped with the broader biflagellate ends projecting outwards. The colonies contain a variable number of cells, but when they reach a certain size division occurs to form two daughter colonies. The cell wall contains numerous siliceous plates which have complex patterns characteristic of different species as revealed by the electron microscope, e.g. *S. petersenii* [16], *S. uvella* [17], *S. sphagnicola* [18] and *S. echinulata* [19].

18

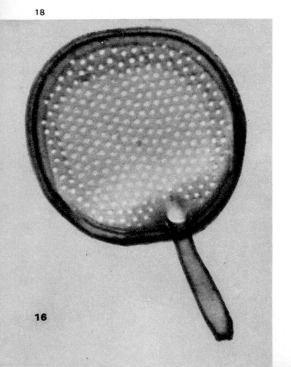

16

19

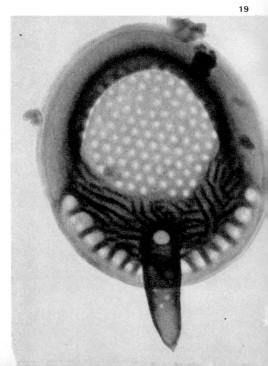

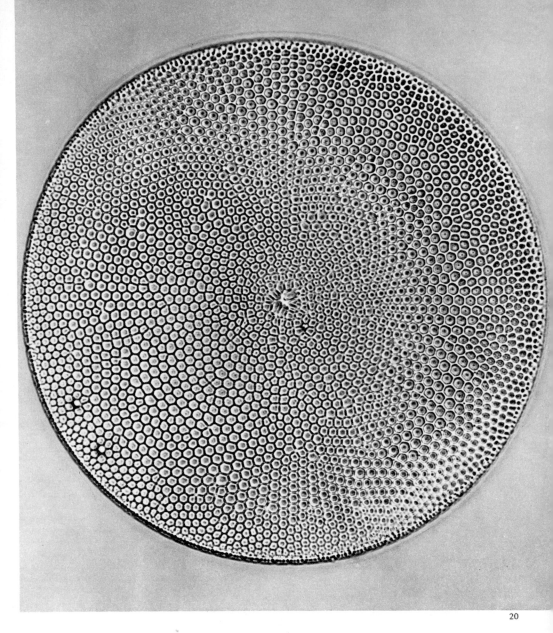

The **Diatoms**, *Bacillariophyta* [20-30], include a larg.
number of microscopic unicellular and colonial
algae which are universally distributed in fresh
water, the sea and the soil. Of particular interest is the
sculptured siliceous wall which makes these plants
particularly beautiful objects under the microscope.
The wall, or frustule, consists of two halves which fit
together rather like the lid and bottom of a box. Some
of them, for example *Coscinodiscus radiatus* [20], are
like a pill-box in shape whereas others are basically
like a date-box, e.g. *Pinnularia viridis* [28]. The surface
or valve view of the former type is usually circular as
in *Arachnoidiscus ehrenbergii* [21] and *Actinoptychus
adriaticus* [22], but it may be triangular with convex
sides, *Triceratium favus* [24], or concave sides, *Trinacria
excavata* [27]. Other, more complex valve forms are
sometimes found, e.g. *Biddulphia pulchella* [23]. The
view of the sides where the edges of the valves fit

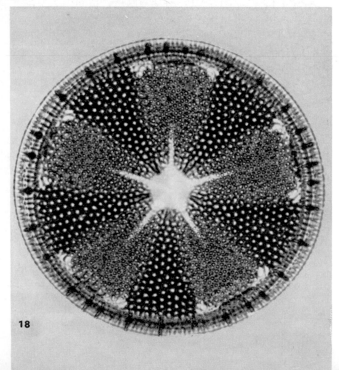

together, the girdle, is generally shortly rectangular. The girdle view of the elongated types is also rectangular but in valve view a variety of shapes is encountered. Three common forms are seen in *Pinnularia viridis* [28], *Diploneis crabro* [29] and *Pleurosigma angulatum* [30]. Many of these have a narrow groove or raphe which lies along the middle of each valve and is filled with cytoplasm.

Living diatoms often exhibit movements which may be slow and continuous or jerky and relatively rapid. Various explanations have been made of the mechanism of this movement but none is completely satisfactory. Many species are found as single cells, either free or attached to a suitable substratum by a gelatinous pad or stalk. Others occur in colonies and are attached to one another in various ways. Some of these colonial forms occur

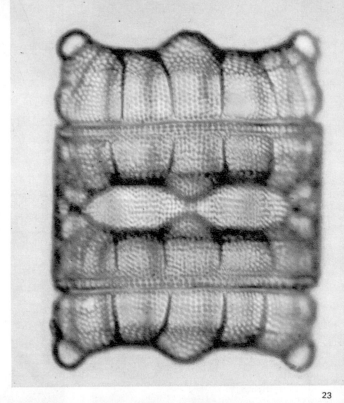

fixed to a support but others are free-floating. Two very common colonial planktonic diatoms of fresh water are *Asterionella formosa* [25], with the extremely narrow cells radiating from a centre, and *Tabellaria flocculosa* [26], in which the plates of cells are attached to one another at the corners. These, together with many single-celled species and other colonial forms, constitute an important element of both fresh- and salt-water plankton.

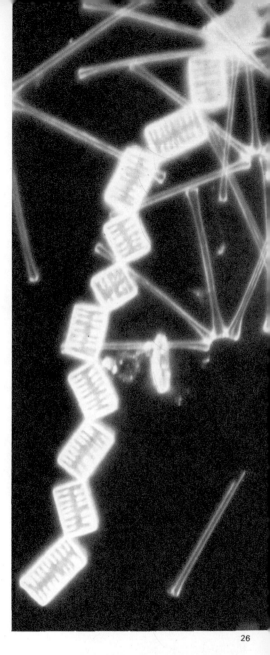

25

26

The pill-box forms are particularly common in marine plankton and sometimes bear long, slender projections which assist flotation.

Each diatom cell contains a nucleus, cytoplasm and one or more pigmented bodies or chromatophores.

These are more or less yellow-brown but in some species they have a greenish tinge. As the cell is bounded by a hard wall, growth by enlargement is limited. When a cell divides the valves separate, and two new ones are formed which fit inside the original ones. In this way one of the daughter cells is the same size as the parent cell and the other is smaller. Diatoms are particularly common in the surface waters of colder seas and form a considerable part of the food of many marine animals. The siliceous walls are almost indestructible and at death they sink and gradually form thick bottom deposits. This process has been going on for millions of years and has resulted in the formation of diatomaceous earths found in various parts of the world. Some of the deposits in the western states of America are up to 300 feet thick and when it is estimated that there may be as many as 40 million frustules in one cubic inch the activity of these tiny plants can be well appreciated.

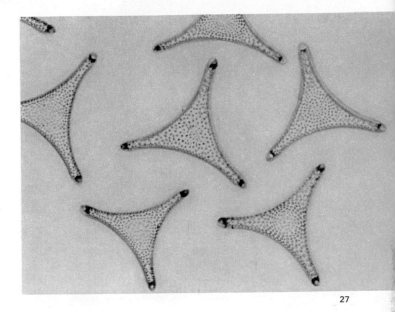

27

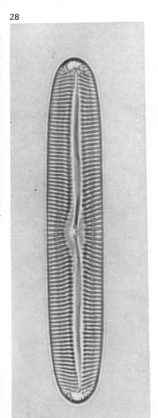

28

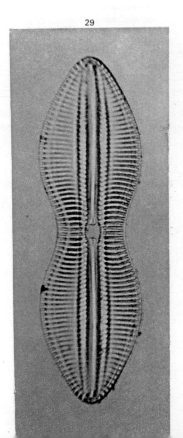

29

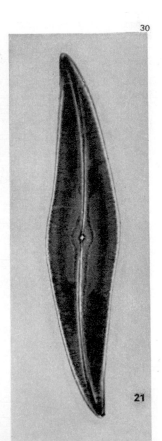

30

21

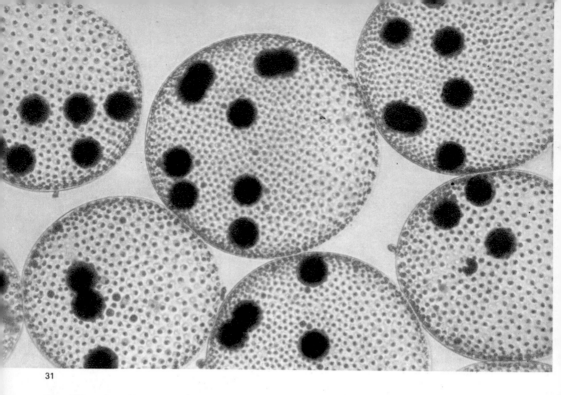

31

The *Chlorophyta* [31-35], the **Green Algae**, includes a wide range of mostly small forms. Some are unicellular, motile or non-motile, but colonial and filamentous types are also found. *Volvox aureus* [31] consists of a hollow sphere with many minute, biflagellate cells embedded in a peripheral gelatinous layer. It moves by the co-ordinated lashing of the flagella; daughter colonies are formed inside the sphere. *Pediastrum duplex* [32] consists of a non-motile flat plate of green cells and *Scenedesmus*

quadricauda [33] has a row of four cells. There are many green filamentous algae. Some are branched but *Zygnema circumcarinatum* [34] has unbranched rows of cells each containing two stellate, green chromoplasts. The desmids, such as *Cosmarium* sp. [35], are very beautiful unicellular green algae which are particularly common in the water of bogs and tarns. The cell is often flattened and consists of two halves each containing a chromoplast. When the cell divides the two halves separate and a new wall is

32

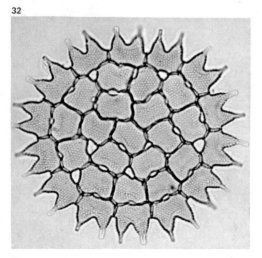

33

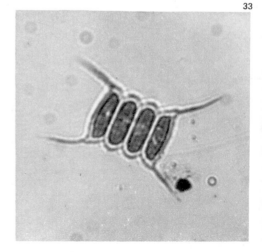

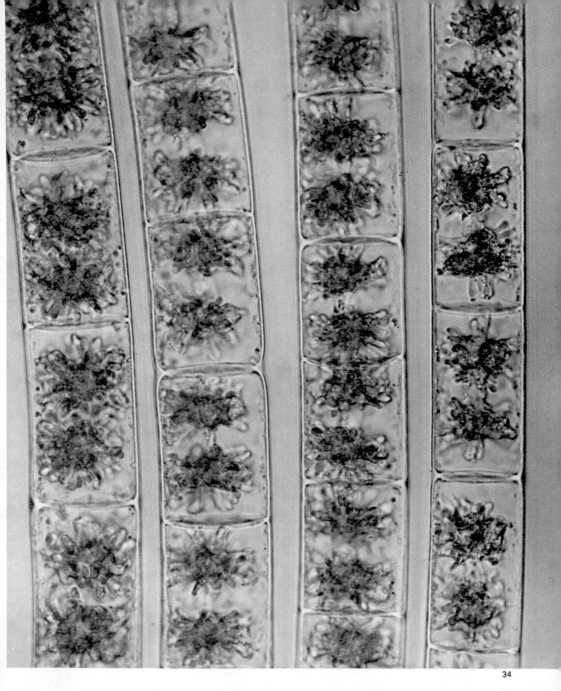

secreted around each projecting portion of cytoplasm so that two daughter cells are formed.

A few seaweeds belong to the green algae, but the majority are either **Red Algae**, *Rhodophyta* [coloured plate I], or **Brown Algae**, *Phaeophyta* [36–38]. The latter group contains chlorophyll but this is masked by the presence of brown pigments. There are no unicellular or motile forms although branched filamentous species which form small dense tufts occur. The majority are large and have a complex

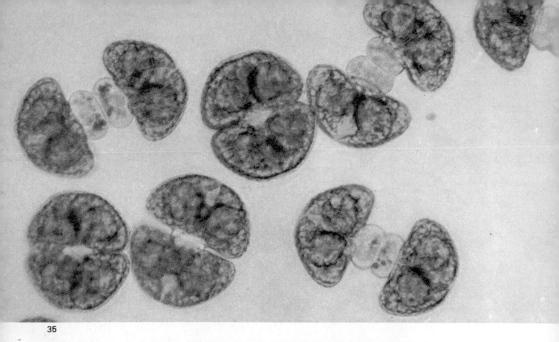

35

36

structure. They are exclusively marine and are particularly abundant in cold temperate seas. Some are free-floating but the majority are securely attached to rocks by a strong hapteron. One of the **Kelps**, *Laminaria cloustoni* [36], together with *L. digitata*, is common on rocky coasts at or slightly below low tide

Ia   *Peyssonelia squamaria* (**Red Alga**)

Ib   *Lithophyllum* sp. (**Red Alga**)

IIa *Agaricus augustus*

IIb *Amanita muscaria* (**Fly Agaric**)

mark. It has a very stout, flexible stalk and a large undulate blade. Fertile regions of the blade bear sporangia and the spores they contain give rise to a minute, short-lived plant which bears sexual organs. The fertilized egg germinates immediately to give rise to the main plant again.

A clear zonation of brown algae can be frequently observed on a rocky shore and the species which occupies the highest level is the small **Channelled Wrack**, *Pelvetia canaliculata* [37]. It has a much-branched thallus with fertile terminal regions. The sexual organs are borne in cavities and the eggs and sperm are released when the plants are covered at high tide. The eggs are fertilized in the sea and germinate directly. This seaweed is exposed for much of the time but can withstand desiccation.

Ascophyllum nodosum [38] belongs to the same family as *Pelvetia* but is found at low levels on the sea shore.

Fermenting **Kafir-corn** or **Kaffir-corn** [39] is a mixture of two bacteria, *Streptococcus lactis* and a *Lactobacillus*, together with a yeast, *Saccharomyces fragilis*. It is used in the production of a native alcoholic beverage in Russia. The same yeast is concerned in the production of Kefir from milk.

The **Slime Moulds**, *Myxomycetes* or *Myxomycophyta* [40, 41], are an interesting group of organisms which have been included in both the plant and animal kingdoms. Like the fungi they are not capable of photosynthesis and reproduce by spores with rigid walls, but the vegetative phase is a naked mass of protoplasm which, like *Amoeba*, can creep over firm surfaces and ingest solid food particles. In fact we have here a group which does not readily fit into our rigid classification of the living world, but in practice the slime moulds are generally studied by botanists. They are most common in cool, moist, shady places and can be found in woods on decaying logs and leaves. They occur mostly in spring and early autumn, particularly after heavy rain. *Lycogala epidendrum* [40] is found widely on rotten wood. The small, round reproductive bodies are soft and red when young but at maturity they are brittle and violet. Eventually they rupture and the minute spores are blown away. *Arcyria nutans* [41] is also common on decayed wood. The deep yellow, cylindrical sporangia are in groups. Each has a fine network within which the spores are produced.

Excluding the bacteria [1-8], slime moulds [40, 41], and lichens [78-82], the *Fungi* [42-77, coloured plate II] consist of between 50,000 and 80,000 species. They do not contain chlorophyll pigments and are unable to synthesize organic food material from water and carbon dioxide. Therefore they must have an external supply of organic substances and live either as saprophytes on dead plant and animal remains or as parasites on living hosts. It is impossible to exaggerate the importance of these organisms both in nature and in man's economy. Saprophytes play an important role in soil fertility by breaking down organic structures, thus making their constituents available to green plants. Many fungal parasites cause serious diseases of important food crops.

The vegetative part of a fungus, the mycelium, consists of a mass of small, colourless, interwoven filaments or hyphae. These grow in and on the substratum, and secrete enzymes which break down the complex food material into simpler, soluble compounds which are absorbed. Reproduction is by the formation of spores and gametes.

The fungi (excluding some groups of uncertain affinities) are divided into three main groups. The *Phycomycetes* are microscopic, non-septate fungi, most of which are aquatic although some, such as potato blight, are parasitic on land plants.

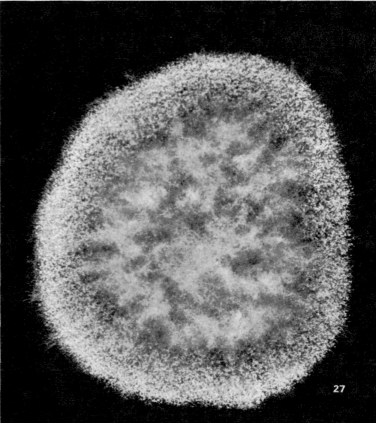

43

In late spring the ascospores of **Ergot**, *Claviceps purpurea* [44], infect the open flowers of grasses, particularly rye, and the fruit is later replaced by a hardened mass of mycelium, the sclerotium. This falls to the ground, and in the following year forms stalked heads containing many asci in cavities. The ascospores are ejected into the air and cause re-infection of the grass. The alkaloids in the sclerotium are very poisonous and can cause serious illness if they get into flour.

The second large group, the *Ascomycetes* [42–47], consists of fungi with a septate mycelium. The characteristic reproductive structure in the group is the ascus, which is usually cylindrical and contains eight ascospores. The genus *Aspergillus* consists of micro-fungi, some of which are important in industry for the production of citric acid. They can be grown in pure culture and when a spore is placed on nutrient jelly a circular colony with the inoculum in the centre is produced [42]. Although under certain conditions some species form asci, reproduction is commonly by the production of enormous numbers of asexual spores or conidia. In *A. fumigatus* [43], which is a cause of a disease in birds, the conidia are produced in chains on the terminal, spherical portion of an erect hypha. They are readily detached and dispersed by air currents.

45

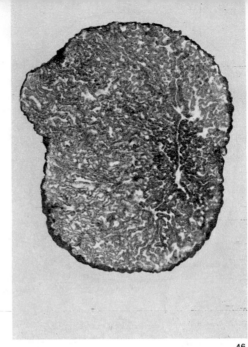

46

The mycelium of the **Morel**, *Morchella esculenta* [45], grows in the soil of woods and pastures. The sporophore, which appears in spring, has a hollow white stalk and a rounded, yellow-brown, sponge-like cap. The cavities of the cap are lined with asci. The Morel is edible and is often used for flavouring soups and stews. It can be used fresh or dried and stored.

Tuber aestivum [46] is one of the **Truffles** which produces its sporophore underground. It grows in beech woods on calcareous soils. The sporophore may weigh four ounces or more and has a black, warty rind. The central mass contains many spherical asci each containing four spores. The ripe sporophore emits a strong odour which probably attracts rodents. In France they are highly valued, and pigs and dogs are trained to find them. *Choiromyces meandriformis* [47] is a rare truffle which produces its large, yellowish-brown sporophores on the soil surface in woods.

47

Most of the fungi with large sporophores, mushrooms, toadstools and bracket fungi, as well as the important parasitic smuts and rusts, belong to the *Basidiomycetes* [48-77]. They have a septate mycelium and reproduction involves the formation of a basidium which produces usually four spores on small projections. *Clavaria vermicularis* [48] is common among the grasses of meadows and pastures, particularly in the early autumn. The cylindrical, brittle, pure white sporophores are two inches or more long and occur in dense tufts. The whole surface is covered with basidia, which shoot their minute spores into the air surrounding the sporophore.

Ramaria botrytis [49] is sometimes found on the ground of deciduous woods during the late summer and autumn. The sporophore has a short, thick stem and numerous erect, irregular, cylindrical branches. It is white with a pink or yellow tinge and the tapering ends of the branches are red. Large specimens may be four inches high and six inches across. The white flesh has a pleasant taste and is considered edible.

48
49

The sporophores of *Phellodon tomentosus* [50] appear in groups on the ground of coniferous woods. Each has a stalk and a leathery dark brown cap with a conspicuous white rim. The numerous fleshy spines that project downwards from beneath the cap are covered with a dense layer of basidia.

Grifola sulphurea [51] attacks the wood of living deciduous trees. The sporophores are produced in groups on the tree trunk. Each is thin, fleshy with a wavy margin, and basidia line the shallow pores on the under surface.

31

Polystictus versicolor [52] is one of the commonest bracket fungi and may be found on dead stumps and fallen branches of various trees throughout the year. The roughly semi-circular sporophores are thin, flexible, from one to three inches across, and often appear in groups. The velvety upper surface is marked with concentric zones, and varies in colour from yellow to dark brown or black, with a pale wavy margin. The white under surface is covered with shallow pores which are lined with basidia.

Trametes rubescens [53] occurs on the fallen branches of deciduous trees, especially willow. The semicircular, bracket-shaped sporophore is from two to four inches across and has a wrinkled, reddish-brown upper surface. The whitish lower surface has numerous radially arranged tubes lined with basidia. Typically the pores are round, but sometimes they are elongated; one such form has been called *Daedalea confragosa*.

Another common bracket fungus is *Trametes gibbosa* [54] which grows on the stumps of deciduous trees, particularly those of poplar, beech and oak. The sporophore is from four to eight inches across and has a hairy, greyish upper surface which often becomes green owing to the growth of microscopic algae. The under surface is white and the pores of the tubes are elongated radially.

In Europe *Fomes fomentarius* [55] is common on the trunks of beech trees, but in Britain it appears to be confined to birch trees in northern Scotland. It has a large, corky, perennial, hoof-shaped sporophore up to 12 inches across. It has a dull, hard outer layer; the brownish-yellow lower surface has many minute round pores. The felt-like flesh of this species was formerly used as tinder.

54

The genus *Boletus* consists
of /fungi with large fleshy
sporophores with a central
stalk and a thick cap which
has long tubes lined with
basidia on the under surface.
Boletus edulis [56] is a large
species found mostly in deciduous woods during the
autumn although the var.
pinicola illustrated occurs in
coniferous woods. It has a
pale, short, stout stalk which
is very swollen at the base; it
is marked with a raised network of white lines towards
the top. The dull brown
rounded cap is from two to
eight inches across and sticky
when young. The long, narrow, white or pale yellow tubes
on the under surface have
small round pores. This is a
valuable edible species.

Boletus scaber [57] is common near birch trees during the summer and autumn. The thick, whitish stalk, covered with blackish scales, is from three to seven inches long. The soft, convex, grey or dark brown cap, from two to six inches across, is sticky when wet. The tubes on the under surface are pale grey. This species is considered good to eat when young.

Gomphidius glutinosus [58, 59] appears in coniferous woods during the autumn. It has a stout stipe from two to six inches long and a convex greyish-brown cap from two to four inches across. A membrane between the edge of the cap and the stem protects the young radiating gills on which the basidia are borne.

60

The fungi included in the family *Agaricaceae* have vertical, radiating gills on the under surface of a cap borne on a central stalk or stipe. The basidia shoot the spores into the spaces between the gills where they fall until carried away by air currents beneath the cap. *Marasmius scorodonius* [60] grows mainly in coniferous woods. It has a slender, smooth, reddish-brown stalk and a thin pale cap. The whole sporophore smells strongly of garlic.

The **Horse Mushroom**, *Agaricus arvensis* [61], is a good edible species found commonly during the autumn in pastures. It has a smooth, stout, whitish stem up to five inches long. A conspicuous double ring on the stalk is the remnant of a membrane which

61

extended to the edge of the cap before the latter expanded. When mature the soft, whitish cap is from six to eight inches across. At first the crowded gills are grey but they gradually turn dark brown as the spores develop.

A. augustus [coloured plate IIa] is a large, yellowish woodland species with a conspicuous ring.

Lactarius fuliginosus [62], which appears on the ground of woods in the autumn, has a brown-tinged stem up to three inches long and a velvety, pale to dark brown cap from one to four inches across. The gills are pale yellow. When cut, the flesh exudes a slightly acrid juice.

The **Shaggy Cap** or **Lawyer's Wig**, *Coprinus comatus* [63], is a common roadside fungus. It has a white, hollow stipe up to 10 inches long and a cap which, cylindrical at first, becomes bell-shaped. As the basidia discharge their spores the gills liquefy.

64

The well-known **Fly Agaric**, *Amanita muscaria* [64, coloured plate IIb], occurs particularly near birch trees and conifers. The stout white stipe has a swollen base and a conspicuous membranous ring near the top. The convex orange-red or scarlet cap is covered with white spots and has crowded white gills underneath. This fungus can cause death if even a small fragment is eaten.

The **Parasol Mushroom**, *Lepiota procera* [65, 68], is a large species found frequently near trees during the summer and autumn. The stout, straight stipe is 10 inches or more long and has concentric brown markings. When young the cap is ovoid and its edge is attached to the stipe [65], but as it expands it leaves a large ring which eventually becomes loose and can be moved freely along the stipe. The greyish-brown convex cap is from four to eight inches across with a raised central region and a thin margin. The soft, crowded gills are white. This is an excellent edible species.

The **Chanterelle**, *Cantharellus cibarius* [66], sometimes occurs in quantity in beech and oak woods during the autumn. It is deep yellow, from one to four inches across, and funnel-shaped with a wavy margin. The thick, shallow gills are often branched. It is an edible species with an odour of apricots when fresh.

The **Grisette**, *Amanita vaginata* [67], is found in heaths and deciduous woods. It has a slender white stalk with a membranous volva at the base and a thin grey cap from two to four inches across.

III   *Liriodendron tulipifera* (**Tulip Tree**)

IVa *Taxus baccata* (**Yew**)

IVb *Nymphaea alba* var. *froebelii*

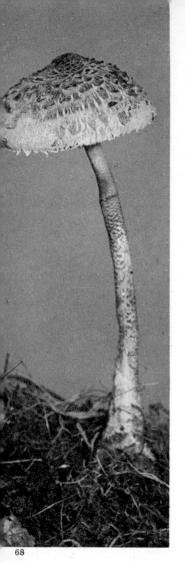

68

An irregular pore appears at the top, and each time a rain drop hits the side wall it causes a thick cloud of spores to be ejected.

Related to the puff-balls are the **Earth-stars**, e.g. *Geastrum pouzari* [70] and *G. recolligens* [71]. They generally occur on the ground in woods. At first they are attached but a thick outer layer splits from the top downwards into a number of segments which curve back to form a stand with the spherical spore-containing structure in the centre. The inner wall is thin, a pore appears at the top, and the spores are released as in the puff-balls.

71

The *Gasteromycetes* include a small number of interesting fungi in which the spores are not forcibly ejected by the basidia. The **Puff-balls** belong here. One of the commonest species, *Lycoperdon perlatum* [69], occurs in pastures and woods during the summer and autumn. The sporophores appear in groups and are about two inches high. Each has a narrow, sterile base and spherical top with a thin wall covered by spines and warts. When mature the upper cavity contains a mass of loose, dry, olive-brown spores.

The **Earth-ball,** *Scleroderma aurantium* [72], is very common in heaths and woods from the middle to the end of the year. The rounded sporophore, from two to three inches across, has no stalk but is attached at ground level to a mycelial cord. The thick, leathery wall has a yellowish-orange, scaly outer surface. The interior is firm and grey at first but eventually the wall breaks open irregularly and the spores are blown away. Another very similar species is *S. verrucosum* which has a thin, smooth, grey-brown wall and a short stalk.

The **Stinkhorn**, *Phallus impudicus* [73–75], is a common species in woods and gardens during the summer and autumn. The whitish spherical or ovoid 'egg' [73], from one to two inches across, is formed just beneath the soil surface at the end of a mycelial cord. It has a thin outer skin and a thick gelatinous layer beneath, both of which rupture at the apex owing to the rapid elongation of the whitish spongy receptacle. Sometimes the skin tears lower down and is carried upwards [74]. The cylindrical receptacle is from four to eight inches long and bears at the top a loose conical cap with a coarse, honeycombed surface. On emergence the surface is covered by a shiny mass of black spores but, owing to the strong foetid smell, flies are attracted to it and within a few hours all the spores are carried away [75]; soon afterwards the whole structure collapses. The smell emitted by this fungus is so strong and characteristic that an emerging sporophore can be detected from many yards away. *Mutinus caninus* is a similar but smaller species.

74

75

43

The **Smuts**, included in the *Ustilaginales*, are important parasites of higher plants. The **Loose Smut** of oats, *Ustilago avenae* [76], is a common and widespread species. The flowers become infected and the mycelium gives rise to a mass of black brand spores. When harvested with the sound grain they are scattered and are sown with the seed. A number of races have been discovered which can attack different varieties of oats. By replacing the grains the fungus seriously reduces the yield.

The **Maize** or **Corn Smut**, *Ustilago maydis* [77], causes irregular swellings of all the aerial parts of the plant including the developing cob. At first these swellings have a white wall of host and fungus tissue but eventually this breaks down to release the dark brown, powdery mass of spores. This smut appears to be able to live and multiply in the soil for some time. The resistant brand spores are dispersed by wind and the fungus can penetrate any young part of the plant.

Lichens [78–82] are common on walls, roofs, rocks, tree-trunks and the ground in humid or dry areas free of atmospheric pollution, and they also occur on pebbles and rocks near the sea. They are remarkable in that they are dual organisms; each lichen is a complex structure involving both a fungus and an alga. Generally the fungus determines the form of the lichen with unicellular green or blue-green algal cells enclosed within its tissues. The fungal component is usually an ascomycete and does not occur in nature independently of the alga, whereas the relatively few algal types involved can exist in the free state. Lichens are small, slow-growing, often crustaceous, and capable of surviving prolonged desiccation.

The genus *Parmelia* includes many common leaf-like lichens which produce simple colourless spores. *P. saxatilis* [78] produces a grey, more or less circular, lobed thallus on trees and rocks.

79

The genus *Cetraria* is close to *Parmelia* but the lobes of the thallus are more erect. The so-called **Iceland Moss**, *C. islandica* [79], which is common on northern heather moors, is one of the few edible lichens. It has more or less erect, reddish-brown thallus lobes about two inches high with rows of marginal black spines. *Cladonia sylvatica* [80] occurs in the wetter parts of heaths and moors. The granular basal parts disappear at an early stage leaving the crowded, richly branched, greyish, erect systems (podetia) which form sponge-like masses. The **Reindeer Moss**, *C. rangiferina*, which is greyish-mauve, is a closely related species. *C. fimbriata* [81] is common on soil and tree-stumps. It has stalked, cup-shaped podetia which have a

80

pale green, granular surface. These granules (soredia) become detached as organs of vegetative reproduction and consist of a mass of fungal filaments and algal cells. *Evernia prunastri* [82] with its forked, green thallus is common on the twigs of bushes and trees.

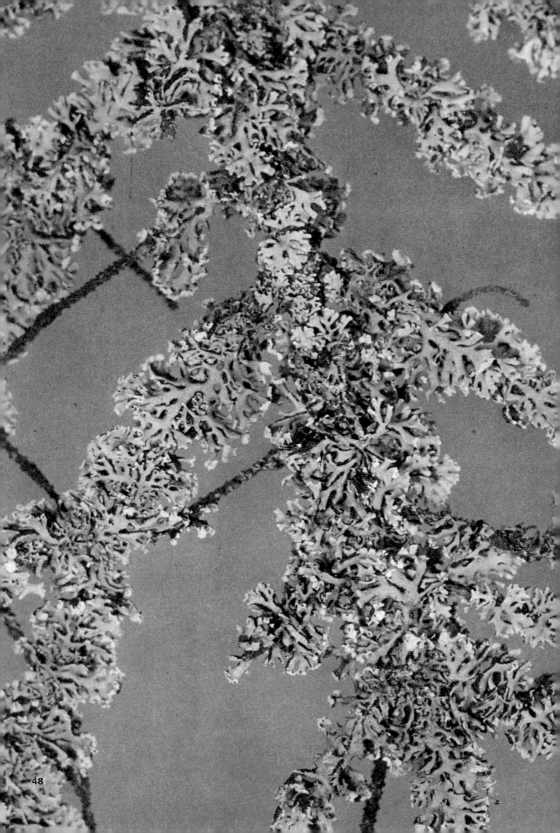

The *Bryophyta* [83–91] include the liverworts and mosses. They are all small plants without roots or woody, water-conducting strands. The green plant is the sexual gametophyte, and after fertilization of the egg a sporophyte is produced. This consists essenti-ally of an unbranched stalk bearing a terminal capsule and it remains attached to the gametophyte. The spores produced in the capsule give rise to a new generation of gametophytes. Some liverworts, for example *Pellia epiphylla* [83], have a flattened,

branched thallus which is closely attached to the ground. Often a large patch is formed in suitable habitats such as the wet shaded banks of streams. The sporophyte has a long, white, fleshy, often curved stalk, and a spherical terminal capsule.

Lophocolea bidentata [84] is one of the leafy liverworts. It is a small plant growing on the soil among the grass of lawns and pastures. The stem is slender and bears two lateral rows of thin, toothed leaves.

84

85

Marchantia polymorpha [85] is a common liverwort with a flattened thallus which has air pores on the upper surface. Vegetative reproduction is effected by means of flat gemmae produced in superficial cups; the sexual organs are developed in stalked heads. The sporophytes appear on the under surface of the female heads and project downwards. Most of the mosses have stems with spirally arranged, simple leaves.

Polytrichum commune [87] is a large moss which often forms large patches on damp moorland. The erect stems are up to eight inches long and bear

51

88

dark green, pointed leaves. The capsules are borne on long wiry stalks and are protected by a hairy hood, the calyptra, until mature. *P. formosum* [86] is a similar species but it usually grows in hedgerows and banks. *Hylocomium splendens* [88] grows most commonly on heaths and moors. It has somewhat flattened shoot systems with red stems and pointed, concave leaves. The plants are unisexual and capsules are not often produced.

Leucobryum glaucum [89] occurs on acid soils in woods and on wet moorland. It has an unusual habit in that it forms conspicuous pale green tussocks

89

from a few inches to two feet or more across, and up to four inches thick.

The spiral arrangement of the crowded, pointed leaves is well seen in the woodland moss *Dicranum polysetum* [90]. *Sphagnum recurvum* [91] is one of the Bog-mosses which often grows submerged in pools. The leaves of the sphagnum mosses absorb and retain water, making them useful in horticulture.

The vast group of vascular plants [92–107] all possess woody, water-conducting tissues. Although the majority of living species produce seeds there are many which reproduce only by means of spores. The life-cycle of these plants is similar to that of the bryophytes but the spore-producing plant is independent and larger than the minute, short-lived, sexual gametophyte. These plants have often been put in the *Pteridophyta* but fossil and other evidence indicates that there are several unrelated groups.

The *Psilopsida* includes only four living plants and, because of lack of fossil remains, ideas of their origin or affinity are purely speculative. *Psilotum nudum* [92] occurs widely in tropical Australasia. It has a slender underground rhizome without roots, and twiggy, ridged, erect, green stems. It has no ordinary leaves but a few small scale-like appendages are present and on some of these are solitary, three-celled sporangia. When released the spores give rise to a small, cylindrical, subterranean gametophyte. Another member of the group is *Tmesipteris tannensis* from Australia and New Zealand, which grows on the trunks of tree ferns.

The *Lycopsida* constituted one of the main elements of the vast forests which covered the land surfaces of the earth during the Carboniferous period approximately 300 million years ago. At that time many were large trees up to 100 feet high but most have become extinct and today the group is represented by less than 1,000 species of small herbaceous plants.

Huperzia selago [93], the **Fir Clubmoss**, occurs on heaths, moors and mountains throughout most of the north temperate zone. It has erect, branched stems from two to 12 inches high, densely clothed with small, lanceolate, dark green leaves. Small, flattened, leafy bulbils are produced and these serve as organs of vegetative reproduction. Periodically the stem will produce a fertile zone with a sporangium on the upper surface of each leaf-like sporophyll.

The **Stag's-horn Clubmoss**, *Lycopodium clavatum* [94], grows in mountainous districts of many parts of the world. It has long procumbent and short ascending stems thickly covered with small, pointed, bright green leaves. The sporangia are borne in dense cylindrical cones up to two inches long which occur terminally on erect stems sparsely covered with scale leaves. The spores give rise to a small, slow-growing gametophyte which may be subterranean and colourless, or on the surface of the soil and partially green. There are about 200 species of *Lycopodium*, many in the tropics being pendulous epiphytes.

93
94

Also included in the *Lycopsida* is the genus *Selaginella* with about 700 species. They produce sporangia in small cones but differ from the other clubmosses by producing two types of spores. Many minute microspores are produced, and fewer megaspores. The gametophyte which develops from the latter is retained within the spore wall and bears the female reproductive organs. The **Lesser Clubmoss**, *Selaginella selaginoides* [95], occurs widely in the north temperate zone, mainly on wet mountain ground. It is a small insignificant plant with slender erect stems bearing spirally arranged leaves. The sporophylls are similar to the leaves; the megasporangia occur at the base of the cone and the microsporangia the top.

The majority of *Selaginella* spp. are tropical plants which thrive only in humid conditions. They have a very characteristic form with the more or less procumbent, slender stems branching in one plane [96]. The leaves are in four rows, the lateral ones being much larger than those on the upper surface of the stem. The crowded, equal sporophylls are also in four rows and give the narrow terminal cones a distinctive appearance. Several species, including *S. kraussiana*, are commonly grown in greenhouses.

The group *Sphenopsida* is represented at the present time by about 25 species of relatively small herbaceous perennials, the **Horsetails**, *Equisetum* spp.

[97–101], but during the Carboniferous period, some 300 million years ago, treelike forms were abundant. The living members have creeping underground

98

99

rhizomes and erect, green, hollow stems which bear whorls of reduced leaves and sometimes, as in the **Great Horsetail**, *E. telmateia* [98], and the **Wood Horsetail**, *E. sylvaticum* [100], whorls of thinner branches. In both *E. telmateia* and *E. arvense* [97], the **Common Horsetail**, the terminal cones are borne on unbranched, pale brown, erect stems in early

spring. In *E. sylvaticum* [99] the cones are borne on green stems which produce lateral branches and persist throughout the summer after the spores are shed. The **Water Horsetail**, *E. fluviatile* [101], produces smooth, erect, green stems which only rarely bear whorls of short lateral branches. Terminal cones are produced on some of the stems in June and

100

101

July. The cones of these species are similar and bear numerous sporophylls on a thick axis. Each sporophyll has several sporangia on the under surface of a flattened terminal head. The minute spores are green and give rise to a lobed, green, bisexual gametophyte. They are common in the north temperate zone.

102
103

There are about 10,000 species of **Ferns** [102–119]. Although predominantly tropical they occur throughout the world and show great diversity of habit. The majority are stout perennial herbs with dissected leaves but some, for example the tropical *Asplenium nidus* [102], have simple undivided leaves. **Bracken**, *Pteridium aquilinum* [103, 104], is the most widespread fern and is particularly common on acid heathland soils. It has extensive underground rhizomes and large leaves from one to 10 feet high. The margins of the ultimate segments of the leaf bear a continuous band of small, brown, stalked sporangia. The spores shed from these develop into a small green prothallus which produces the sex organs. After fertilization a new plant is produced.

105

Most ferns belong to the order *Filicales* but there are some which are best included in other orders. One of these, *Angiopteris erecta* [105], belongs to the order *Marattiales*, a group of large, primitive tropical and subtropical ferns. It has long, pinnately compound leaves which arise from a short, thick, vertical stem. The **Royal Fern**, *Osmunda regalis* [106], in the order *Osmundales*, is separated from the rest of the ferns. It grows in wet heaths and bogs and is found in many parts of the world including the British Isles and eastern North America. It is a handsome plant with a short, erect stem and pinnate leaves from one to eight feet long. The upper, brown parts of the leaves are fertile and bear clusters of small sporangia.

There are over 200 species of **Tree Ferns**, *Cyathea* spp. [107], which grow in tropical and subtropical regions. The plant has an erect, straight trunk covered with roots and leaf bases and a terminal crown of pinnately compound leaves. Some species reach a height of 60 or 70 feet.

Cheilanthes marantae [108, top right] grows in dry rocky places in southern Europe. It has a creeping rhizome and stalked, pinnate leaves up to a foot long which are covered beneath with pale brown scales. The **Rusty-back Fern**, *Ceterach officinarum* [108, bottom left], also grows on dry rocks and walls from the British Isles to the Himalayas. It is a small fern with a short rhizome and simple, pinnate leaves from one to eight inches long. The linear groups of sporangia occur on the under surfaces of the leaves among the brown overlapping scales.

The **Ostrich Fern**, *Matteuccia struthiopteris* [109], occurs in northern, central and eastern Europe. It has soft, bright green, sterile leaves up to five feet long and short, erect, fertile leaves.

108

109

65

110

111

The **Hard Fern**, *Blechnum spicant* [110], grows in woods and on heaths and moors on non-alkaline soils throughout much of Europe, temperate Asia and western North America from California to Alaska. It has a short, thick rhizome and numerous sterile, smooth, spreading pinnate leaves from four to 20 inches long. The fertile leaves are erect, up to 30 inches long, and have blackish stalks and very narrow green pinnae. The sporangia are borne on the under surfaces of the pinnae in continuous lines one on either side of the midrib.

The **Black Spleenwort**, *Asplenium adiantum-nigrum* [111], grows on rocks, hedge-banks and walls throughout most of Europe except the eastern and far northern areas. It has a short rhizome covered with dark brown scales when young. The reddish-brown leaf-stalk is from two to 10 inches long and the triangular, thick, bipinnate blade is about the same length. The elongated groups of sporangia (sori) lie along a vein on the under surface of the leaf segments and are protected by lateral flaps (indusia). The genus *Asplenium* includes about 650 species. Two common and widespread species on rocks and walls are the **Maidenhair Spleenwort**, *A. trichomanes*, and the **Wall Rue**, *A. ruta-muraria*.

The **Stag's-horn Ferns** belong to the genus *Platycerium*. There are about 15 species in tropical Africa, Malaya and Australia, including *P. alcicorne* [112]. They are all epiphytic on tree trunks or grow on steep rock surfaces. The short rhizome has two kinds of leaves. Shield-shaped mantle leaves are applied more or less closely to the support and the organic debris which collects behind them is used as a 'soil'; roots grow into it and absorb water and mineral salts. The pendulous, forked leaves are green; the sporangia occur in large brown patches on their under surfaces.
The **Hart's-tongue Fern**, *Phyllitis scolopendrium* [113], grows in shady woods and hedgerows throughout much of temperate Europe and Asia and in a few places in North America. It has a short rhizome and linear-lanceolate leaves from four to 24 inches long. The linear sori occur in pairs on the under surfaces of the leaves. Hybrids between this species and the **Black Spleenwort** have been recorded.

The **Male Fern**, *Dryopteris felix-mas* [114], is widespread throughout Europe and temperate Asia. It has an erect rhizome and more or less spreading, dissected leaves which are from one to five feet long. The circular sori occur on the under surfaces of the ultimate leaf segments and when young are protected by a kidney-shaped indusium.

The **Holly Fern**, *Polystichum lonchitis* [115], occurs in rocky places, often on mountains throughout much of the arctic and north temperate regions. It has a short, stout, ascending rhizome and stiff, persistent, simply pinnate leaves from three to 24 inches long. The deep green leaf segments are slightly curved and have sharply toothed margins. The small round sori are in two rows on the under surface of the pinnae, one on either side of the midrib. Each sorus is protected by a circular, toothed indusium.

Polypody, *Polypodium vulgare* [116], is an aggregate species widespread in the north temperate region. A number of forms have been distinguished but the status of these has not been definitely established. It grows on damp rocks and walls and on the branches of trees. It has a stout, creeping rhizome and linear-lanceolate, pinnatifid or pinnate leaves from two to 18 inches long. The circular or elliptical sori occur in two lines on the under surface of the leaf segments and are not protected by indusia.

115

116

69

The majority of ferns are terrestrial but two small groups, the *Salviniales* and *Marsileales*, are aquatic. *Azolla caroliniana* [117] is an American species which has become naturalized in Europe. It is a small floating plant with slender stems, bluish-green bilobed leaves borne in two rows, and simple roots. It produces two types of spores and reproduction is complicated. *Salvinia natans* [119] is also a floating aquatic with thin, branched stems. The leaves are in whorls of three, two of each whorl being ovate, green, and covered on the upper surface with papillae, and the third submerged, finely divided, and root-like. It is an annual in nature and the reproductive structures are formed at the base of the submerged leaves. In a warm greenhouse it may overwinter without producing sporangia. There are about 10 species of *Salvinia* spp. in tropical and warm temperate regions. Rapid development of *Salvinia* over many square miles of the artificial Lake Kariba in Africa has become a serious problem in recent years.

Marsilea quadrifolia [118] is a semi-aquatic perennial with a slender, creeping rhizome and leaves with long stalks each bearing four terminal leaflets. It varies greatly in stature depending upon the degree of inundation. The basal, stalked reproductive structures, sporocarps, have hard ovoid coverings and contain two types of sporangia.

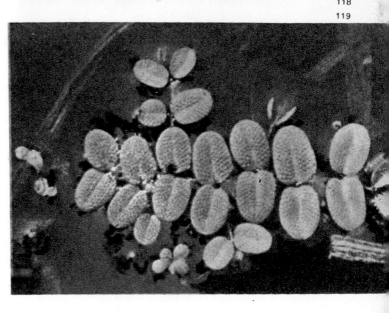

118
119

71

The Gymnosperms [120–175] are vascular plants, i.e. they contain woody conducting tissue; but unlike living ferns they produce seeds [120]. These seeds are exposed and are seldom completely enclosed within an ovary as are those of the flowering plants or Angiosperms (p. 101). The living Gymnosperms, of which there are about 650 species, represent at least two evolutionary lines that can be traced back many millions of years from the evidence of their fossil remains. Today the bulk of living members of the group are conifers which are put in the order *Coniferales* [120–165]. This is divided into several families of which the largest is the *Pinaceae* which includes a number of important north temperate conifers.

The **European Silver Fir**, *Abies alba* [121, 122], like most conifers, has an embryo in the seed with several seed leaves or cotyledons which become the first green leaves of the seedling [121]. It is an evergreen tree attaining a height of 150 feet with blunt, flat, dark green leaves up to an inch long. The male and female cones are borne on the same tree, and pollination is effected by wind. When mature the female cone [122] is from four to six inches long and has two winged seeds on the upper surface of each scale. This species is native on the mountains of central and southern Europe.

121
122

123

124

The **White Fir**, *Abies concolor* [123], occurs in the Rocky Mountains of southern Colorado and ranges southwards to New Mexico and Mexico, and westwards to California and Oregon. It reaches a height of from 100 to 150 feet and the flattened glaucous leaves, from two to three inches long, are curved outwards. The cylindrical cone is from three to five inches long when mature.

The **Noble Fir**, *Abies procera* [124], forms large forests mainly on the Cascade Mountains in Washington, Oregon and northern California. It can reach a height of 250 feet and the trunk a girth of 24 feet. The dense, more or less glaucous leaves are flattened, about an inch long, and have rounded tips. In cultivation the mature cylindrical cones can be up to 10 inches long and four inches across. As in all the 30

125

126

or so species of *Abies*, the seeds are shed when the cones break up, leaving the bare axis attached to the tree.

The **Douglas Fir**, *Pseudotsuga menziesii* [125], occurs over vast areas of western North America in southern British Columbia, Washington, Oregon, California, Arizona and the Rocky Mountains. Under the most favourable conditions it can grow to over 300 feet and have a trunk 40 feet in circumference. The thick, corky bark is deeply grooved; the thin, dark green leaves are about an inch long. The light brown,

mature cones are from two to four inches long; beneath each seed scale is an upwardly projecting, three-lobed bract. The two other American members of the genus are the smaller **Colorado Douglas Fir**, *P. menziesii* var. *glauca,* and the **Large-coned Douglas Fir** or **Big-cone-spruce**, *P. macrocarpa,* of California. The **Eastern Hemlock**, *Tsuga canadensis* [126], is a native of eastern North America. It reaches a height of 100 feet. The flattened leaves are less than an inch long. The stalked, ovoid cones are from $\frac{1}{2}$ to one inch long, and the winged seeds are small.

127

The **Common Spruce**, *Picea abies* [127], has a wide distribution in Europe from the Pyrenees to western Russia. It reaches a height of 200 feet in central Europe. The stiff leaves, quadrangular in section, are from ½ to one inch long and often all curved to one side of the stem. The pendulous brown cones are cylindrical, from four to six inches long. The cone scales separate in the spring, releasing the winged seeds. There are a large number of curious forms of this variable tree in cultivation. Some are small, globose or prostrate bushes; in others the lateral branches are short and the branchlets pendulous [128].

129

The **Servian Spruce**, *P. omorika* [129], is confined in nature to a small limestone area of Yugoslavia. It is a tall, slender, spire-like tree with shiny, flattened leaves. The ovoid cones are up to two inches long.

130

131

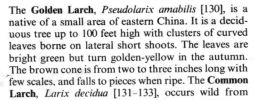

The **Golden Larch**, *Pseudolarix amabilis* [130], is a native of a small area of eastern China. It is a deciduous tree up to 100 feet high with clusters of curved leaves borne on lateral short shoots. The leaves are bright green but turn golden-yellow in the autumn. The brown cone is from two to three inches long with few scales, and falls to pieces when ripe. The **Common Larch**, *Larix decidua* [131–133], occurs wild from central Europe to Siberia and is extensively planted elsewhere for its valuable timber, and for ornament. It is a deciduous tree up to 150 feet high with clusters of narrow leaves about an inch long borne on lateral short shoots [131]. The soft female cones are pinkish at pollination time [132 left] but become brown and woody. The scales separate to release the seeds, but the cones remain on the tree for some time [133].

132

133

134

The **Atlas Cedar**, *Cedrus atlantica* [134], is confined to the Atlas mountains of Morocco and Algeria. It reaches a height of 120 feet and when well developed is a graceful tree with horizontal branches. It is evergreen, and the needle leaves, which are often glaucous and up to an inch long, are borne on the young extension shoots and in tufts on short woody laterals. At the time of pollination the female cones are small [137], but when ripe they are erect, brown, woody structures up to three inches long [135]. They break up and the seeds are released.

Two similar species are the **Deodar**, *C. deodara*, from the western Himalayas and Kashmir, and the **Cedar of Lebanon**, *C. libani*.

135

136

The largest genus in the family is *Pinus* with about 80 species. They are all evergreens with needle-like, green leaves which are borne in groups of two, three or five at the ends of dwarf shoots.

The **Arolla Pine**, *P. cembra* [136, 139], occurs in two widely separated areas, at high altitudes on the Alps of central Europe and at much lower levels in Siberia. It reaches a height of 120 feet in the wild. The stiff, erect leaves, about three inches long, are borne in groups of five. The erect, ovoid, purplish-brown cones are from two to three inches long and are broken apart by animals searching for the seeds.

137

138

82

140

141
142

The **White** or **Weymouth Pine**, *Pinus strobus* [138],
is widely distributed in Canada and the northern
United States. It reaches a height of 150 feet and has
narrow, bluish-green leaves from three to five inches
long in groups of five. The pendulous, cylindrical,
often curved cones are from four to six inches long.
The thin scales curve back at maturity, releasing the
winged seeds.

The **Scots Pine**, *Pinus sylvestris* [140, 141], is widespread in Europe and temperate Asia and is the only
native pine in the British Isles. It is widely cultivated
in the United States. It reaches a height of 100 feet or
more and has two-needled dwarf shoots. The small
male cones occur in dense clusters on young extension
shoots [140]. The mature, brown, female cones [141]
are conical, from two to three inches long.

The variable *P. nigra* [142], which includes the
Austrian and Corsican Pines, is a native of southern
Europe, Asia Minor and Morocco. It is a pyramidal
tree up to 150 feet high with pairs of dark green needle
leaves up to six inches long. The ovoid-conical cones
are yellowish-brown. The **Austrian Pine**, subsp. *nigra*,
with almost straight, dull green leaves, extends from
Austria to Crete, but the **Corsican Pine**, subsp. *laricio*,
with paler, twisted leaves, is a native of south-western
Europe. These also are extensively cultivated.

143

The **Mountain Pine**, *Pinus mugo* [143,145], grows on rocky slopes and moorland areas in the mountains of central and southern Europe. It differs from most pines in often developing as a thick prostrate shrub, although in the Pyrenees it can attain a height of 80 feet. The pairs of stiff, curved, dark green leaves are from two to three inches long. As in other pines, the clusters of cylindrical male cones [145] are produced in late spring and the female cones are ripe about 26 months after pollination. The ovate, brown cones are from one to two inches long and contain small seeds. Although of little value for timber this species is very hardy, and has been planted for stabilizing sand dunes and as a protective screen for other trees.

The **Northern Pitch Pine**, *Pinus rigida* [144], grows extensively in eastern North America from New Brunswick to Georgia and westward as far as Kentucky and Tennessee. It is a tree from 50 to 80 feet high with a slender trunk and spreading, horizontal branches. The stiff, slightly curved leaves are up to four inches long and are borne in threes. Often adventitious buds produce tufts of leaves along the trunk. The ovoid, pale brown cones are about two inches long, and occur in clusters. They tend to remain closed on the tree for many years before opening to release the seeds. This species is valuable for planting on poor soils but its timber is inferior to that of *P. palustris*, known as the **Pitch Pine** in Europe and as **Longleaf Pine** in America. The latter species is also a native of eastern North America. It has cones from six to 10 inches long.

144

145

Kahikatea, *Podocarpus dacrydoides* [146], is a native of New Zealand. It is an evergreen tree from 50 to 150 feet high with small, flat or scale-like leaves. The trees are unisexual and, as in other members of the family *Podocarpaceae*, the solitary small seeds are enclosed in a fleshy, round receptacle.

The **Swamp Cypress**, *Taxodium distichum* [147, 148], grows in wet ground and shallow water in the southeastern United States. It is a handsome deciduous tree up to 150 feet high. The leafy branchlets are shed as a whole in the autumn. The globose cones are about an inch across and produce few, wingless, triangular seeds.

The **Big Tree**, *Sequoiadendron giganteum* [149, 150], is confined in nature to a few small areas in California in the Sierra Nevada. It attains a height of well over 300 feet, and a girth of 90 feet. The reddish-brown, fibrous bark is up to two feet thick, and the small overlapping leaves are scale-like. The ovoid cones [150] have few scales and produce flattened seeds each with two lateral wings.

146

147

87

149

The **Dawn-redwood**, *Metasequoia glyptostroboides* [151], was discovered in a small area of central China in 1945; until that time the species was known only from fossil remains. It is now known as a "living fossil" and is flourishing in many parts of the world.

The **Chinese Fir** or **China-fir**, *Cunninghamia lanceolata* [152], is an evergreen tree up to 150 feet high from central and southern China. The flattened, curved leaves are up to three inches long. Each scale of the ovoid mature cone bears three flattened seeds.

151

152

88

Va   *Nelumbo nucifera*

Vb   *Victoria cruziana*

VIa   *Paeonia suffruticosa*

VIb   *Mediolobivia ritteri*

153

The **Chile Pine** or **Monkey Puzzle**, *Araucaria araucana* [153], is a native of Chile, Tierra del Fuego and northern Patagonia. It reaches a height of 150 feet and has a slender, cylindrical trunk and whorls of spreading branches. The stiff, pointed, dark green leaves persist for ten or 15 years. The globose cone is up to seven inches long; on breaking up each scale is shed with the seed attached to the upper surface.

154

155

The **Incense Cedar**, *Libocedrus decurrens* [154], is a native of the western United States from Oregon to California. It is a columnar evergreen tree up to 150 feet high with flattened branchlets covered with dark green scale leaves. The cylindrical, pendulous cones are ¾ inch long and have six scales. Each scale bears one or two winged seeds. The soft durable wood is fragrant.

The **Hiba Arbor-vitae**, *Thujopsis dolabrata* [155], is an important Japanese forest tree. It is an evergreen up to 100 feet high and often has a curved trunk. The flattened branchlets bear overlapping leaves which are dark green above and marked with white patches below. The woody, globose cones are about ¾ inch across and produce a few small, winged seeds.

Thuja occidentalis [156], the **American Arbor-vitae** or **White-cedar**, forms large forests on swampy ground in eastern North America. It reaches a height of 60 feet and the branchlets are covered with scale leaves which emit a strong odour when bruised. The brown, pendulous cones are about ½ inch long; a few winged seeds are borne on only two pairs of scales.

The **Chinese Arbor-vitae**, *Thuja orientalis* [157], from northern and western China, is a dense evergreen bush or small tree up to 40 feet high. The branches and branchlets tend to be erect; the dark green leaves are very small and scale-like. The ovoid woody cones are about an inch long and each of the six or eight scales has a recurved terminal spine. Two or three ovoid, wingless seeds are produced on the lower scales.

The **Mediterranean Cypress**, *Cupressus sempervirens* [158, 159], the cypress of classical literature, grows wild on mountains of the eastern Mediterranean regions, and is widely planted in southern Europe, particularly Italy. It reaches 150 feet in height and may have a spreading or columnar habit. The slender spreading branchlets are covered with minute green leaves arranged in four equal rows. The shiny brown or grey globose cone [159] is about an inch across. Each of from eight to 14 woody scales bears from eight to 20 small winged seeds on its upper surface. This tree grows to a considerable age, and the fastigiate form is frequently grown in gardens and cemeteries in Italy. The fragrant wood is also used for clothes chests.

The **Hinoki Cypress**, *Chamaecyparis obtusa* [160], is a native of central and southern Japan where it is used extensively for forest planting. It is an evergreen tree up to 120 feet high with a straight trunk and reddish-

157
158

brown bark. The dense
branches are spreading, and
the flattened branchlets are
covered by the overlapping
leaves in four rows. The leaves
are of two sizes, blunt, and
have obvious white markings
on the under surface. The
stalked spherical cones are
about ½ inch across. They
usually have seven or eight
woody scales, each of which
bears from two to five winged
seeds.

The **Nootka Cypress**,
Chamaecyparis nootkatensis
[161], occurs on the western
coastal region of North
America from Alaska to
Oregon. It attains a height of
120 feet in America, and has
flattened, pendulous branchlet
systems. The dull green,
pointed, scale-like leaves emit
a pungent odour when
bruised. The spherical, green,
purple-tinged cone is about ⅓
inch across and the outer
surface of each of from four
to six scales bears a triangular
tooth. Two flattened, winged
seeds are borne on each scale.

162

163

Juniper, *Juniperus communis* [162], is widespread in arctic and north temperate regions. It is a shrub or small tree up to 30 feet high, with short linear leaves in whorls of three. The plants are unisexual. The cone is a globose, blue-black, berry-like structure containing from one to six seeds. The **Savin**, *J. savina* [164], is a shrub up to 15 feet high which usually grows on limestone and is widespread in central and southern Europe and the Caucasus. Its place is taken in North America by the similar **Red-cedar**, *J. virginiana*.

The **Yew**, *Taxus baccata* [163, 165, coloured plate IVa], occurs widely in Europe, the Himalayas and North Africa. In the British Isles it is found mainly on calcareous soils. It is a slow-growing evergreen tree up to 70 feet high with a reddish-brown bark and

164

94

165

flattened linear leaves about an inch long. The trees are unisexual and the small axillary male cones [163] are surrounded by several scales. On the female tree the seeds are solitary and at maturity are surrounded by a cup-shaped, fleshy, red aril [165, coloured plate IVa]. Many forms are known in cultivation.

Other gymnosperms, not included in the *Coniferales*, include about 30 species of low, evergreen shrubs [166-175]. *Ephedra major* [166], which is found from the Mediterranean region to Northern India, is about six feet high and has dense, dark green branches bearing scale leaves. The plants are unisexual and have male and female 'flowers'. The so-called fruit is red and about $\frac{1}{4}$ inch long. Several species are characteristic of North American deserts.

The **Maidenhair Tree**, *Ginkgo biloba* [167-171], probably no longer exists in the wild state. It has been planted in China and Japan since earliest times, particularly near palaces and temples. It was introduced into Europe in 1730 and is now widely grown in temperate countries. It is a slender deciduous tree up to 100 feet high, although weeping forms [167] are

166

167

95

known in cultivation. The thin, long-stalked, fan-shaped leaves are from two to four inches across and are produced in clusters each spring on short lateral shoots [168]. Usually the leaf blade is notched at the tip. The trees are unisexual, and the pollen-producing structures are borne in cylindrical catkins on the short shoots of the male tree [169]. Each structure consists of a short stalk with a terminal knob having two backward-projecting pollen sacs attached to it. On the female tree, stalked pairs of exposed ovules are borne on the short shoots [170]. After pollination these develop into yellow seeds with a fleshy outer layer [171]. This outer layer breaks open when the seeds fall, and produces an offensive smell. It is therefore best to use male trees for planting by roadsides, though unfortunately there is no reliable way of recognizing the sex of the tree until it produces reproductive structures, by which time it is too big to transplant easily. There are records of single trees producing both male and female structures, but it seems likely that this has been the result of grafting.

168

169

The **Maidenhair Tree** is unlike any other living plant. Although its general habit and anatomy are those of a conifer, it has motile male sperms similar to those produced by the cycads (p. 98). The fossil record indicates that the evolutionary line to which it belongs is a long one, stretching back at least 200 million years. In fact fossil leaves indistinguishable from those of the existing species are found in rocks of the Jurassic period which were laid down about 180 million years ago. It is for this reason that *Ginkgo* has been called a living fossil, and but for the attention given to it by Buddhist priests it would probably by now be extinct.

172

The *Cycadales* [172–174] include about 100 species with a scattered and often very restricted distribution in tropical and subtropical regions. They represent the remnants of a large group of plants that flourished in the Mesozoic era about 200 million years ago. Most are like tree-ferns in habit, with an erect, thick, rarely branched stem covered with leaf bases and a crown of large pinnate leaves, e.g. in *Cycas revoluta* [172] which occurs from Madagascar to Japan. Some species are small, with underground stems, and others attain a height of 70 feet. They all produce abundant pollen in the male cones, which are usually large and more or less woody, e.g. in *Dioon edule* [173] from Mexico. The plants are unisexual, and in all except *Cycas* spp. the ovules, which develop into seeds after fertilization, are borne marginally on the scales of the female cones, e.g. in *Ceratozamia mexicana* [174] from south-east Mexico.

Welwitschia mirabilis [175] is one of the most remarkable plants known. It occurs in a few restricted desert regions of tropical west Africa. Although it may live for 100 years or more it only ever has two leaves, which continue to grow from the base where they are attached to the top-shaped woody stem as the tip is continually being worn away. The plants are unisexual and the 'flowers' are borne in stalked, ovoid spikes. The naked seeds are enclosed in the persistent winged perianth and are wind-dispersed.

174
175

176

In the Flowering Plants or *Angiospermae* the ovules are almost always completely enclosed in the ovary of the flower. After fertilization the ovules develop into seeds which are released from the fruit or shed with it. Both the seeds and the fruits [176] vary greatly in form and size.

178

The *Magnoliaceae* are a small family of 10 genera and about 100 species. Over 70 species are included in the genus *Magnolia*. All are woody trees or shrubs with simple alternate leaves and large bisexual flowers. Quite frequently, as in *M. denudata* [177] from China, the flowers appear before the leaves. An X-ray photograph of a flower of this species [178] shows clearly the basic floral structure found in the family. The overlapping petaloid perianth parts are inserted separately at the base of the elongated floral axis. Above these are many free spirally arranged stamens and the terminal region is occupied by many free carpels. These features of the flower have led many botanists to believe that the *Magnoliaceae* are one of the most primitive of existing families of flowering plants. This view is supported by its scattered distribution in eastern North America, the West Indies, Brazil, eastern Asia and Malaya.

179

180

A number of species of *Magnolia* are grown for ornament, including the Japanese *M. obovata* [179] with fragrant cup-shaped flowers which appear in May.

The **Tulip-tree**, *Liriodendron tulipifera* [colour plate III], from the eastern United States is also a member of the *Magnoliaceae*. It is a deciduous tree up to 100 feet high with alternate, truncate leaves. The flowers have six petals coloured greenish-white with orange blotches. The cone-like fruit [180] consists of a group of elongated achenes each containing a single seed.

The Old World **Pitcher-plants** belong to the small family *Nepenthaceae*. There are about 60 species of *Nepenthes* which occur mainly in Borneo although some are found in south China and Australia. They are mostly herbaceous climbing plants with inconspicuous, greenish, unisexual flowers. They are of great interest because of their complicated pitcher leaves [181]. Each of them has a short basal stalk, a flattened region and a long curved portion ending in an erect pitcher with incurved rim and a complicated lid. The inner surface of the pitcher is smooth, and insects which enter are drowned in the water present in the bottom of the pitcher and are digested by enzymes secreted by special glands in the wall. For the American Pitcher-plants, see the *Sarraceniaceae* (p. 132).

VII *Astrophytum myriostigma*

VIIIa *Conophytum meyeri*

VIIIb *Portulaca grandiflora*

182

183

The large widespread tropical **Pepper** family, *Piperaceae* [182, 183], includes over 1,300 species, for the most part herbs or shrubs with entire, alternate leaves. The minute greenish flowers are usually bisexual but have no petals or sepals and are borne singly in the axils of bracts on long fleshy spikes. Each small fruit contains a single seed.

The genus *Piper* occurs in the tropical regions of both hemispheres and is the largest in the family with over 700 species. The most important species is *Piper nigrum*, which comes from Java and is the source of commercial pepper. The unripe fruit yields black pepper; white pepper is obtained from the fruit when it is completely ripe. The stems of *Piper tiliifolium* [182], a native of Mexico, are sometimes used to make walking sticks. The **Japanese Pepper**, *P. fatokadsura*, is a deciduous climbing plant which can cling to walls with its aerial roots. The leaves of **Betel**, *P. betle*, are used to wrap round pieces of betel nut, the fruit of a palm, *Areca catechu*, which is often chewed in the East. The genus *Peperomia* [183], with over 600 species of annual or perennial herbs, is also found in both hemi-

spheres but occurs predominantly in tropical South America and Mexico. It is of no economic importance, but a number of species are grown as indoor plants for their foliage. Identification is difficult owing to their variability and the fact that many rarely flower. The **Water-lily** family, *Nymphaeaceae* [184–193, coloured plates IVb, V], consists of about 90 species in three distinct groups which may be considered as separate families. The water-lilies are fresh-water plants widespread in tropical and temperate areas. They are mostly large rhizomatous perennial herbs with submerged or floating leaves. The long leafstalks contain many air spaces which assist flotation and they may be flexible, so that floating blades remain on the surface with changes of water level. The beautiful solitary flowers appear at or somewhat above the surface of the water. The number of sepals and petals present varies with the genus but they are always free from each other and sometimes spirally arranged. Usually there are many free stamens and the gynoecium is variable.

The **Yellow Water-lily** or **Brandy-bottle**, *Nuphar lutea*

184

185

[184, 185], is common in Europe and northern Asia and occurs throughout the British Isles in ponds and streams. It has a thick branched rhizome and both floating and submerged leaves. The flower [184] has several greenish-yellow sepals and numerous smaller yellow petals which bear nectaries. The gynoecium is flask-shaped and has a flat top with radiating stigmatic surfaces. The fruit [185] has an alcoholic smell and matures above the water. When ripe it bursts and segments of the inner tissue containing numerous small seeds break free and float away. The common American **Spatterdock** is *Niadvena*.

186

The **White Water-lily**, *Nymphaea alba* [186, 187], is a native of Europe and the British Isles. It has a stout rhizome buried in the mud and circular floating leaves. The flower [187], which opens on the surface of the water, has four sepals and 20 or more white petals which grade into the numerous stamens. The ovary has many chambers and is sunk in the floral receptacle. The fruit, which ripens under water, eventually splits open owing to the swelling of mucilage and the numerous buoyant seeds float free. There are a number of red-flowered varieties of *N. alba*, including var. *froebelii* [coloured plate IVb].

187
188

There are about 40 species of *Nymphaea*, including
the **Egyptian Lotus Flower,** *N. lotus* [188, 190]. This
has toothed leaves and the white flowers are borne
well above the water surface on long slender stalks.
Other species, and also hybrids, are cultivated including *N. rubra* with red flowers and *N. mexicana* with
yellow flowers.

The **Sacred Lotus** of India is *Nelumbo nucifera*
[coloured plate Va]. Both the large leaves and rose-
coloured flowers are carried above the water surface.
When ripe the curious fruit consists of a disk-shaped
receptacle with a number of hard nuts contained in
separate pits on the upper surface. There is only one
other species of *Nelumbo*, the yellow-flowered *N. lutea*
from the eastern parts of North America.

191

192

193

The genus *Victoria* includes two closely related water-lilies which grow profusely in the back-waters of South American rivers. They are *V. amazonica* [189] and *V. cruziana* [coloured plate Vb] which were formerly included in the single species *V. regia*. The circular floating leaves [189] are up to seven feet in diameter and have up-turned edges which prevent water getting on to the top. Owing to the network of thick veins underneath [191] and the heavily cutinized upper surface [192] they are so strong that they are able to bear the weight of a child without sinking. The flowers [193] are borne on thick prickly stalks a few inches above the surface. They can be more than a foot in diameter.

110

The **Barberry** family, *Berberidaceae* [194–198], includes about 10 genera and 300 widespread species, mainly in north temperate regions.

The **Oregon Grape**, *Mahonia aquifolium* [194], is a native of western North America but is frequently cultivated in Britain and has become naturalized in places. It is an evergreen shrub up to four feet high with alternate, pinnate leaves which have stiff, dark green, spiny leaflets. The small, yellow, fragrant flowers appear during early spring in dense erect terminal clusters. The subglobose fruit is a purplish berry. There are about 50 species of *Mahonia*, most of which come from North America or eastern Asia. Among those cultivated in Britain are *M. japonica* from Japan with strongly scented flowers and *M. fremontii* from the southern United States with very spiny greyish leaves.

194

195

196

197

198

The genus *Berberis* includes over 200 species, most of which are natives of South America or central and eastern Asia. The **Common Barberry**, *B. vulgaris* [195–197], is widespread in Europe and occurs throughout the British Isles. It may be a true native in some parts of England but has been planted for its edible fruits and the limits of its natural range are obscure. Moreover, it has been eradicated as far as possible because it is the alternative host for the stem rust of wheat. It is a shrub from three to eight feet high with yellowish grooved twigs which bear divided spines [195]. The simple obovate leaves occur on very short axillary shoots. The yellow globular flowers [196] are borne in dense pendulous clusters in May and June. The stamens are interesting in that they promptly curve inwards when lightly touched. The oblong fruits [197] are red when mature.

The **Barren-worts**, *Epimedium* spp., are rhizomatous herbs. Several species, including *E. macranthum* [198] from Japan and *E. alpinum* from southern Europe, are cultivated.

The **Peony** family, *Paeoniaceae*, was formerly included in the *Ranunculaceae* (p. 114) but is distinguished on features of anatomy and structure of the fruit. It is confined to about 50 species of the genus *Paeonia*, most of which occur in central Asia although some are found in southern Europe and two species are natives of western North America. They are large perennial herbs or shrubs with spirally arranged, segmented leaves. The conspicuous terminal flowers have numerous free parts and are usually white, pink or red. The fruit [200] consists of from two to five thick-walled follicles each of which splits along its inner edge to release the few large shiny blue seeds. The so-called **Tree Peonies** have been derived from *P. suffruticosa* [199 and colour plate VIa], a woody species which is a native of north-east Asia. *P. lactiflora* is also from the same region and is the origin of most of our cultivated herbaceous forms, although other species and hybrids are also grown. Showy double varieties with numerous petals replacing the stamens are frequently planted in gardens.

199

200

113

The **Buttercup** family, *Ranunculaceae* [201–228], includes about 1,500 species found mainly in the cooler regions of the northern hemisphere. They are mostly herbs with alternate leaves but some are woody or have opposite leaves. The flowers usually possess many spirally arranged, free parts, a feature which is considered primitive. Modifications related to pollination are common. Most members of the family contain poisonous alkaloids, some of which are used medicinally. Many species are also cultivated for their attractive flowers.

The **Christmas Rose**, *Helleborus niger* [201], is a native of central and southern Europe. It is often cultivated and flowers in midwinter. The leathery, toothed leaves are dark green and the beautiful flowers are pure white or tinged with pink. It has five petaloid sepals and the numerous petals take the form of small tubular nectaries. The fruit is a group of follicles containing numerous seeds. All species of *Helleborus* are highly poisonous. They generally grow on calcareous soils. Two species widespread

201
202

203

in Europe, including Britain, are the **Stinking Helle-bore**, *H. foetidus*, and the **Green Hellebore**, *H. viridis*. The **Winter Aconite**, *Eranthis hiemalis* [202], is a native of southern Europe which has become naturalized over much of Britain. It is a perennial herb with a tuberous rhizome. The flowers appear early in the year, before the leaves. Three palmately lobed bracts form a conspicuous green frill just beneath the flower, which has six yellow sepals, about the same number of nectaries and numerous stamens. The group of brown, many-seeded follicles are mature in May and the leaves have disappeared by the end of June.

The **Marsh Marigold** or **Kingcup**, *Caltha palustris* [203], is common in marshes, damp woods and other wet places throughout most of the north temperate zone. It is a very variable perennial herb with a thick rhizome, smooth erect stems and round, more or less toothed leaves. The flowers appear in small groups during the spring; each possesses from five to eight yellow perianth segments, numerous stamens, and up to 13 carpels. Nectar is secreted by patches on the walls of the carpels. The follicles are still green when they open to release the numerous seeds.

There are over 50 species of **Columbines**, *Aquilegia* spp. *A. nigricans* [204] is a native of central and south-east Europe. It is a perennial with biternate leaves and terminal, nodding, purplish or dark blue flowers. The five sepals are petaloid and the five petals have long backwardly projecting spurs which contain nectar. The fruit is a group of many-seeded follicles.

205

The **Globe Flower**, *Trollius europaeus* [205], is widely distributed in north temperate areas in wet pastures and woods and on sheltered rock ledges up to 8,000 feet. It is a variable species, the small form illustrated being subsp. *transsilvanicus*. Each flower has approximately 10 petaloid sepals, from five to 15 hidden nectaries, together with numerous stamens and carpels. The follicles contain shiny black seeds.

Nigella damascena [206], a native of southern Europe, is the popular garden annual known as **Love-in-a-mist.** The divided leaves have linear segments and the bracts beneath the solitary terminal flower are similar. The flower has five blue petaloid sepals, five nectaries and numerous stamens. The carpels are joined

206

and in the fruit form an inflated spherical capsule.

Isopyrum fumarioides [207] is a native of eastern Asia which is occasionally cultivated. It is a tufted perennial with solitary white flowers and leaves similar to those of Fumitory. *I. biternatum* is an attractive wild flower of eastern North America.

The **Tatra Larkspur**, *Delphinium oxysepalum* [208], is confined to alpine and subalpine levels of the west Carpathians. It is a perennial with deeply dissected, dark green leaves and terminal spikes of flowers. Each flower has five bluish-violet petaloid sepals and four small petals. Two of the petals have nectar-secreting projections which lie in the backward-pointing spur of the upper sepal. The fruit is a group of follicles containing winged seeds. Many striking species of Delphinium are natives of North America.

207

The **Monkshoods**, of the genus *Aconitum*, include a number of closely related and variable species. *A. vulparia* [209] is widespread in central and southern Europe. It is a perennial with palmately lobed leaves. The yellow flowers are bilaterally symmetrical and two stalked nectaries are enclosed in the upper 'helmet' of the petaloid calyx. The fruit consists of three follicles. Other species have blue flowers; several of these are native in North America. All contain poisonous alkaloids.

210

211

212

Thalictrum aquilegifolium [210] is a **Meadow Rue** found mainly in central and eastern Europe. It is a perennial with divided leaves and erect clusters of flowers. The few small perianth parts soon fall leaving the numerous conspicuous stamens exposed. The fruit is a small head of one-seeded achenes. There are several common North American species.

The annual *Adonis aestivalis* [211] has very dissected leaves and bright red flowers. It is a native of central and southern Europe but sometimes appears as a cornfield weed elsewhere. The flowers have five sepals and each petal has a red spot at its base. The fruit is an elongated head of achenes.

Anemone sylvestris [212], which occurs in central and eastern Europe, is a perennial with palmately divided basal leaves. The long flower stalk has a whorl of leaf-like bracts some distance below the solitary terminal flower. The flower has 5 white perianth parts but no nectaries are present.

The **Wood Anemone**, *Anemone nemorosa* [213], is widespread throughout Europe and the British Isles in deciduous woods. It has an extensively creeping rhizome and the simple erect flowering stems appear in early spring before the leaves. The flowers are similar to those of *A. sylvestris* but are smaller and have six or seven perianth parts. *A. quinquefolia* and *A. virginiana* are similar North American species.

214

215

Adonis vernalis [214], unlike *A. aestivalis* [211], is a perennial; the flowers have from 10 to 20 narrow yellow petals. It is widespread in Europe and western Asia.

Hepatica nobilis [215] is a small perennial found throughout most of Europe. It is similar to species of *Anemone* but has evergreen leaves and the whorl of small entire bracts is situated immediately beneath the flower. The ovate perianth segments are usually blue but may be pink, white or purple. The North American *H. americana* and *H. acutiloba* are closely related.

Anemone narcissiflora [216] is widespread in alpine and subalpine pastures on the mountains of Europe and Asia. It is a perennial with deeply dissected basal leaves. Each erect

216

flowering stem has a whorl of segmented bracts and a terminal umbel of from three to eight flowers. The five or six perianth parts are whitish and flushed with pink on the outside.

The **Pasque Flowers** are often included in the genus *Anemone* though many botanists now put them into the separate genus *Pulsatilla*. They differ from other Anemones in having persistent styles which form long feathery appendages to the achenes. They are tufted perennial herbs often covered with dense silky hairs. Numerous species have been described but they are extremely variable, often with many distinct local populations. *P. vernalis* [217] is widespread in western and southern Europe. The basal evergreen leaves have short stalks and from three to five toothed segments. The bracts beneath the flower are divided into narrow lobes. The flower is about two inches across and the perianth segments are whitish within but flushed pink or blue on the outside.

P. halleri occurs in dry pastures up to 5,000 feet in the Alps, the Carpathians and on the mountains of the Balkans and the Crimea. Five subspecies, separated on variations of leaf form and stature, have been described. They occupy different regions, subsp. *slavica* [218] being confined to the western Carpathians. The flower bud is protected by numerous lanceolate bracts. When open it is from two to three inches across and has six purplish perianth parts.

220
221

P. pratensis is another species widely distributed in central and eastern Europe. The nodding flowers are cylindrical with the tips of the perianth parts reflexed. Flower colour is variable, those of the northern form subsp. *nigricans* [220] being dark purple. White-flowered plants, f. *pallida* [219], are occasionally found.

P. vulgaris is an extremely variable species found in eastern England, northern and central Europe and western Asia. The dissected leaves of subsp. *grandis* [221] do not appear until the heads of plumed achenes are developing.

P. patens is familiar on the prairies and mountains of western North America.

The **Traveller's Joy** or **Old Man's Beard**, *Clematis vitalba* [222, 223], is a perennial woody climber found growing in hedgerows and scrub, often on calcareous soils. It occurs in England, central and southern Europe, North Africa and the Caucasus. Most of the leaves have five leaflets; the leaf stalks twine around the branches of other plants, thus gaining support. The scented creamy-white flowers are borne in dense clusters. The fruit is a large head of plumed achenes. Several other similar species occur in North America.

The **Creeping Buttercup**, *Ranunculus repens* [224], is abundant in wet grassland and is a weed throughout the British Isles, Europe and temperate Asia. It produces extensive rooting runners which enable it to occupy exposed ground very rapidly. The flowers usually have five sepals and five petals and the fruit is a head of compressed achenes.

A number of the 300 species of *Ranunculus* are mountain plants, including *R. parnassifolius* [225] which is found in northern Spain, the Pyrenees and the Alps. It is a small perennial rarely more than four inches high with white flowers about an inch across. The **Alpine Crowfoot**, *R. alpestris* [226], is widespread among wet calcareous rocks on mountains of central and southern Europe. It is a perennial with small, round, lobed leaves. The saucer-shaped flowers, which are borne on erect stems from three to six inches high, have five white, slightly cleft petals.

222
223

127

Also included in the genus *Ranunculus* are the **Water Crowfoots**. They are aquatic or marsh plants which, as in the widespread European and North American *R. aquatilis* [227], may have both flattened floating leaves and finely divided submerged leaves. The flowers are white and borne an inch or two above the surface of the water. These aquatic species are extremely variable and are difficult to identify unless flowers and fruits are available. The **Lesser Celandine**, *R. ficaria* [228], is found in woods and meadows throughout the British Isles, Europe and western Asia. It is a small plant which perennates by means of root tubers, and in one subspecies by axillary stem tubers as well. The flower has three sepals and from eight to 12 narrow yellow petals. It is often found as a weed in North America.

224
225

226

The **Poppy** family, *Papaveraceae* [229-234], includes about 100 species of the northern hemisphere. All parts of the plants contain latex. The flowers are bisexual and usually have two sepals, four petals, and many stamens.

The **Californian Poppy**, *Eschscholizia californica* [229], with divided leaves and solitary dark-red to cream-coloured flowers, is a favourite garden annual which is sometimes found as a garden escape'.

Chelidonium majus, the **Greater Celandine** [230], is widespread in hedgerows in Britain, Europe, northern Asia and parts of North America. It is a perennial herb with pinnate leaves and an orange latex which contains poisonous alkaloids. The loose clusters of bright yellow

129

229
230

130

flowers appear during the early summer. The fruit is an elongated capsule containing shiny black seeds each of which has a fleshy white appendage.

The **Yellow Horned Poppy**, *Glaucium flavum* [231], is found mostly on coastal shingle banks in Britain, Europe and eastern North America. It has a long, thick tap-root and coarsely lobed, hairy leaves. The yellow flowers are up to two inches across and appear between June and September. The fruit is a narrow curved capsule up to a foot long.

Several wild species of *Papaver* occur in Britain and others are cultivated. The **Field Poppy**, *P. rhoeas* [232], is a common cornfield weed in Britain and Europe which has been introduced into America and Australia. It is a variable annual herb with bright red flowers. The minute seeds are released through pores around the top of the capsule.

P. somniferum, the **Opium Poppy** [233], is a variable plant. The lilac-flowered form is often grown in gardens but it is the white-flowered subspecies which is extensively cultivated for the opium obtained from the unripe capsules. The **Oriental Poppy**, *P. orientale* [234], is a coarse perennial with bright scarlet flowers up to six inches across.

231

232

233

234

The **Fumitory** family, *Fumariaceae* [235, 236], includes over 400 species of north temperate herbaceous plants. It is closely related to the *Papaveraceae* but the small flowers are zygomorphic.

Corydalis cava [235] with purple flowers is a native of central and southern Europe which is sometimes cultivated. More commonly grown, especially in damp soil, is **Bleeding Heart**, *Dicentra spectabilis* [236], a native of China with pink flowers.

The *Sarraceniaceae* [237, 238] are a family of about 10 species of North American **Pitcher-plants**. In *Sarracenia purpurea*, a species widely naturalized in central Ireland, the leaves [237] have the form of elongated funnels which act as insect traps. The solitary flowers [238] are purple.

235

236

237

The **Caper** family, *Cappari-daceae*, widespread in tropical and subtropical regions, is composed of about 700 species.

The capers used for flavouring are the dried flower buds of *Capparis spinosa*, a Mediterranean species. *C. coriacea* [239] is a species from South Africa. The **Spider Flower**, *Cleome spinosa*, is a frequently cultivated annual, and widespread in North America.

The 70 species of the **Mignonette** family, *Resedaceae*, occur mainly in the Mediterranean region. The **Wild Mignonette**, *Reseda lutea* [240], with lobed leaves, is widespread in Europe and frequent on waste ground in England. **Dyer's Rocket**, *R. luteola,* a similar plant with entire leaves, was formerly used as a source of a yellow dye. The fragrant **Mignonette**, often grown in gardens, is derived from a North African species, *R. odorata*.

133

241
242

243

The **Cress** family, *Cruciferae* [241–253], includes about 2,000 species of annual and perennial herbs. They are found in many kinds of habitats and although widely distributed are mainly north temperate. The family is of great economic importance for food crops which include turnip, cabbage, cauliflower, radish, watercress and mustard. Many species are grown as ornamental garden plants and a number are common weeds of cultivation. The bisexual flowers are small and possess four sepals, four petals which are often yellow or white, and usually six stamens. The fruit generally opens by two valves and its size and form are important diagnostic features.

White Mustard, *Brassica alba* [241], is probably a native of the Mediterranean area but has become naturalized in many countries, including Britain. It is used as fodder and green manure as well as for the mustard produced from the seeds. It has bright yellow flowers and narrow fruits.

The **Hoary Cress**, *Cardaria draba* [242], is also a Mediterranean species which has become widely distributed and is now a pernicious weed in Britain. It is a perennial with a long tap-root. The small white flowers are borne in dense clusters and the short fruit, which contains only one or two seeds, does not open.

245

246

247

Cardamine pratensis [243], the **Cuckoo Flower** or **Lady's Smock**, is common throughout north temperate regions; in Britain and North America it occurs mainly in damp situations. It is an extremely variable species with pink or sometimes white flowers. The long, narrow fruit opens violently, flinging the seeds up to six feet away.

The **Perennial Candytuft**, *Iberis sempervirens* [244], is an evergreen with narrow, dark green leaves. The dense flat clusters of white flowers appear in early spring. The petals on the edge of the cluster are considerably larger than the rest. The short, flattened fruit contains two winged seeds.

Thlaspi arvense [245], the **Field Penny-cress**, is a common weed of arable land throughout the northern hemisphere. The white flowers are very small but the flattened circular fruits are nearly an inch across and contain from 10 to 20 seeds.

Shepherd's Purse, *Capsella bursa-pastoris* [246], which can be found in flower at any time of the year, is a cosmopolitan weed of cultivation. It is a variable species and distinct local populations are often established owing to self-pollination. The flattened triangular fruit contains over 20 seeds.

Berteroa incana [247] is an east European species which has become naturalized in waste places throughout Britain, Europe and North America. It has white flowers and small elliptical fruits.

The **Yellow Whitlow Grass**, *Draba aizoides* [248], is a small alpine plant found on calcareous rocks in central and eastern Europe. It occurs in one place on the south coast of Wales but is doubtfully native there. The short, flat, elliptical fruit contains numerous seeds. Many other species occur in North America. *Petrocallis pyrenaica* [249], which forms small dense tussocks, is another alpine plant which grows on limestone in the Pyrenees, Alps, Carpathians and Croatian mountains.

249

The **Garden Arabis**, *Arabis caucasica* [250], is a short perennial with pale greyish-green leaves and white, scented flowers. It is often cultivated in rock gardens and is sometimes found naturalized. It is a native of mountains in the Near East and Mediterranean region. Many species of *Arabis* are native in North America. *Alliaria petiolata* or *Alliaria officinalis* [251], **Garlic Mustard, Sauce-alone** or **Jack-by-the-Hedge**, is widespread in Europe and Asia and is a common hedgerow plant in Britain; it is naturalized in North America. It is a biennial with pale green leaves which smell strongly of garlic when damaged. The terminal groups of white flowers appear in spring. The long narrow fruit contains numerous blackish seeds.

The **Golden Alyssum** or **Basket - of - Gold**, *Alyssum saxatile* [252], is a native of central Europe but is commonly cultivated. The dense clusters of small, bright yellow flowers appear in spring.

Matthiola incana [253], the **Garden Stock** or **Gilliflower**, is probably a native of southern Europe or northern Africa but has become widespread through cultivation. Double forms are grown and the **Ten Week Stock** is a distinct variety. The **Night-scented Stock** is *M. bicornis* and the **Virginia Stock** is *Malcomia maritima*.

139

254

255

Jacquinia smaragdina [254] belongs to the small tropical American **Joewood** family, *Theophrastaceae*. It is a woody plant with simple crowded leaves and greenish flowers.

The family *Myrsinaceae* consists of about 1,000 species of trees and shrubs mainly distributed in tropical and south temperate regions. *Ardisia paniculata* [255] is a woody evergreen from Assam which is sometimes grown in warm greenhouses for its white flowers and bright red fruits. The **Primrose** family, *Primulaceae* [256–268], includes about 600 species of annual and perennial herbs. They are widely distributed but are most abundant in north temperate regions. The leaves are usually simple and borne in opposite pairs or basal whorls. The flowers have five fused petals and five stamens opposite the corolla lobes. Many species are grown for ornamental purposes.

The genus *Primula* contains some 250 species, many of which are attractive mountain plants. In most there are two types of flowers, some with a long style and low stamens (pin-eyed) and others with a short style and high stamens (thrum-eyed). This assists cross-pollination by insect visitors.

The true **Oxlip**, *P. elatior* [256], occurs in Europe and western Asia and also in a few southern English counties. It is somewhat intermediate between the **Primrose**, *P. vulgaris*, and **Cowslip**, *P. veris*, and can be confused with the hybrid between these two species which is also known as **Oxlip**.

Primula minima [257] is a tufted plant about two inches high with deep pink flowers which grows in the eastern

Alps, Sudeten mountains, Carpathians and the Balkan peninsula. *P. denticulata* [258] is a native of the Himalayas which is frequently grown in gardens. The attractive spherical heads of blue flowers are produced in early spring. The **Chinese Primrose**, *P.* *sinensis* [259], has been grown as an ornamental plant for many years and its origin is obscure. The **Alpine Auricula**, *P. auricula* [260], is also extensively cultivated for its fragrant yellow flowers. It grows on calcareous rocks on central European mountains.

257

258

259

260

Androsace alpina [261] is a small plant with pink flowers which grows at high elevations in the Alps on non-calcareous detritus. The **Shooting-star**, *Dodecatheon meadia* [262, 266], is a handsome plant which has been in cultivation for many years. The flowers, like those of a cyclamen, have reflexed petals. **Sowbread**, *Cyclamen purpurascens* [263], grows on mountains of Europe on calcareous soils. It has an underground tuber and the pink flowers are borne singly on long stalks.

261

262

Soldanella montana [264] grows at alpine and sub-alpine elevations in the Pyrenees, Alps and Balkan mountains. It can push the heads of attractive mauve flowers through the covering of snow.

263

264

Cortusa matthioli [265] is widespread but rare on the mountains of Europe and Asia. The terminal clusters of dull red flowers are borne on slender stems. The **Yellow Pimpernel**, *Lysimachia nemorum* [267], is a slender, creeping perennial. It occurs in Europe and western Asia and is common in woods throughout the British Isles. **Creeping Jenny** or **Moneywort**, *L. nummularia*, is a similar, stouter plant. Other species of *Lysimachia* are erect perennials, for example *L. punctata* [268] which is a frequently cultivated native of eastern Europe. Several attractive species grow in North America.

265

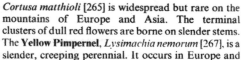

266

The large **Cactus** family, *Cactaceae* [269–287, coloured plates VIb, VII], includes between 1,200 and 1,800 species but the number and limits of genera are not clear. They are entirely New World plants with the dry areas of Mexico as their main centre of distribution. They extend as far south as Patagonia and northwards into the United States where native species occur in every state except Vermont, New Hampshire and Maine.

The cacti are perennial, fleshy, herbaceous or woody plants with a watery sap. A few have fleshy leaves but in the majority the leaves are vestigial. In many the stem is greatly enlarged, succulent, cylindrical or flattened, sometimes jointed and covered with characteristic groups of bristles and spines.

The bisexual flowers are usually solitary and showy with numerous brightly coloured perianth parts and spirally arranged stamens.

268

269

270

271

The fruit is a berry containing numerous seeds.
The few species of *Pereskia* are the least cactus-like members of the family. *P. bleo* [269] is a small tree with stiff broadly lanceolate leaves and axillary spines. The pinkish flowers are borne in terminal clusters. This plant is a native of Panama but is sometimes cultivated in other warm regions or in hothouses. It is often confused with *P. grandiflora* from Brazil; and owing to its reddish young shoots it is put in the genus *Rhodocactus* by some authorities.

Rhipsalis cassytha [270] is a pendulous epiphyte which grows on trees in Florida, Mexico and Central

272

America. It has also become completely naturalized in tropical Africa, Mauritius and Ceylon. The pale green cylindrical stems are profusely branched and form a cluster up to 10 feet long. The small cream-coloured flowers are formed laterally on the terminal joints. The fruit is a berry similar to that of the Mistletoe.

The **Agave Cactus**, *Leuchtenbergia principis* [271],

is a native of Mexico. It has a short woody trunk bearing spreading fleshy tubercles two to four inches long. At the end of each tubercle is a group of twisted papery spines, the central one being longer than the others. The widely expanded flowers have numerous petals and are borne near the ends of young tubercles. The fruit contains many dark brown seeds.

The genus *Astrophytum* includes a number of

273

274
275

spherical or cylindrical cacti which do not usually have spines. *A. asterias* [272] is a native of Mexico. It is globular with longitudinal grooves separating the rounded lobes of which there are usually eight. Down the middle of each lobe is a row of circular woolly areoles. The large flower, which has numerous yellow petals and stamens, is borne near the top. *A. myriostigma* [coloured plate VII] is also from Mexico. It usually has five acute ribs which are covered with a variable quantity of whitish scales and have a row of median woolly areoles. The large flowers are yellow. There are numerous varieties occurring both naturally and in cultivation, some of which have only four lobes, for example *A. myriostigma* var. *tetragonum* [273].

Lophophora williamsii [274] is a native of Texas and Mexico. It is more or less globular and usually has eight shallow lobes. The small flowers are white or pink. This is the **Mescal Button** or **Peyote** which is highly valued by various Mexican tribes, containing several narcotics which produce a feeling of exhilaration. The tops are dried and the Aztecs called these **Teonancatyl.** Similar symptoms are produced by certain mushrooms which Mexican natives gather and eat, dried.

The genus *Echinocactus*, e.g. *E. eyriesii* [275], in the broad sense includes a large number of cylindrical, strongly ribbed and spiny cacti found abundantly in Mexico and extending farther into both North America and into South America. Recently this group has been divided among more than 20 different genera.

276

There are about 130 species of *Opuntia* widespread from Canada to southern South America. They grow mostly in dry regions but a few occur in wet places. They vary greatly in size from spreading trees up to 20 feet high to small prostrate forms. Included here are the familiar **Prickly Pears** with flattened, ovoid, jointed stems and **Cholla**, the branched woody species. They bear raised areoles each of which has a small pointed leaf, usually one or several spines and numerous barbed bristles. It is the latter that are easily detached and cause intense skin irritation. Several are cultivated including *O. gosseliniana* var. *santa-rita* [276] and the **Indian Fig**, *O. ficus-indica*, which has edible fruits.

277

The areoles, which are believed to be reduced branches, take many forms. They may bear many spines as in *Mammillaria microheliopsis* [277] or a few large curved ones as in *Ferocactus cowillei* [278]. In the **Hatchet Cactus**, *Pelecyphora aselliformis* [279], they look like wood-lice crawling on the stem.

In recent years these bizarre plants have become popular and are now grown in greenhouses in many parts of the world. Many are not difficult to cultivate and their wide range of habit [280] and beautiful flowers, for example *Mediolobivia ritteri* [coloured plate VIb], are of interest. *Pseudoespostoa melanostele* [281] is an extremely rare species from the Peruvian Andes with woolly cylindrical stems.

IXa   *Peltiphyllum peltatum*

IXb   *Bougainvillea spectabilis*

Xa *Geum × borisii*

Xb *Rubus idaeus* (**Raspberry**)

282

Among those most easily grown are species of *Epiphyllum* and *Phyllocactus* with flattened, jointed stems [282]. There are many cultivated forms with beautiful flowers. *Ancistrocactus scheeri* [283] from Mexico has tubercles tipped with radiating spines of which the central one is long and hooked. The small flowers are

283

284

greenish-yellow. *Brachycalycium saglione* var. *tucumanense* [284] has rounded tubercles with few short spines.

285

The genus *Rebutia* includes several small species of South American cacti which are easily grown and raised from seed. *R. violaciflora* [285], which has large flowers for the size of the plant, is a native of Argentina and Bolivia. *Gymnocalycium mihanovichii* var. *friedrichii* [286], with sharp ribs and pale yellow

286

287

288

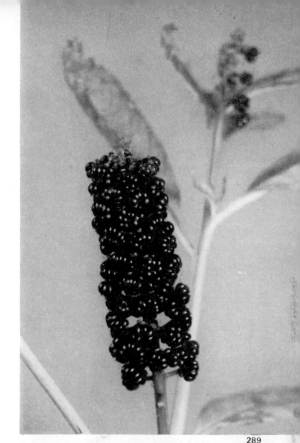

flowers, comes from the same region. Members of the genus *Mammillaria*, for example *M. aureilanata* [287], are cylindrical cacti covered with spiny tubercles.

Most of the 125 species of the **Pokeweed** family, *Phytolaccaceae* [288–291], are found in the American tropics. They may be herbs, shrubs or trees and always have simple, entire, alternate leaves. The flowers are usually small, bisexual and borne in dense elongated inflorescences. Each flower has four or five sepals, generally no petals, and a variable number of stamens and carpels. The fruit also varies in different genera. The largest genus is *Phytolacca* with about 35 species. The **Pokeberry** or **Pokeweed**, *P. americana* [288, 289], occurs in North America. It has shiny reddish-black berries which are used for colouring wines and sweets. The young shoots are occasionally used as a vegetable. Apart from this species the family is of no economic importance although a few are cultivated as ornamentals. One of these, the tropical *Rivina laevis* [290, 291] which has white flowers and dark red fruits, is occasionally grown in hothouses.

The small family *Nyctaginaceae* is confined mainly to tropical and sub-tropical regions of the New World. It includes the beautiful climber *Bougainvillea spectabilis* [coloured plate IXb].

155

The *Aizoaceae* [292–297], sometimes known as the *Mesembryanthemaceae*, is a large family of about 600 species centred mainly in South Africa although some members are found in Australia and America. They are succulent annual or perennial herbs with fleshy leaves containing water storage tissue and often grow in arid stony areas. Like the *Cactaceae* (p. 146). many have large attractive flowers. The bisexual flower has several green sepals but no petals, the apparent corolla being composed of the sterile, petaloid outer stamens. Usually a number of fertile stamens are also present. The fruit is a capsule which may remain closed until soaked by rain so that the seeds are released in conditions favourable for germination.

Many members of the family are cultivated as ornamentals. Both *Delosperma echinatum* [292] with prickly, elliptical leaves and yellow flowers and *Lampranthus productus* var. *lepidus* [293], which has smooth cylindrical leaves and white flowers, are natives of South Africa. *Ruschia maxima* [294] has

292

293

opposite pairs of curved fleshy leaves. The leaves of *Faucaria lupina* [296], which are also in opposite pairs, have bristly margins. Most remarkable are the species

294

296

297

with only two mottled fleshy leaves. These plants are very difficult to find in the stony places where they grow except when they produce their showy flowers.

Examples are *Lithops gracilidelineata* [295], *Conophytum meyeri* [coloured plate VIIIa] and *C. tumidum* [297].

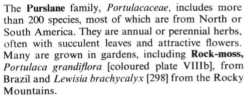

The **Purslane** family, *Portulacaceae,* includes more than 200 species, most of which are from North or South America. They are annual or perennial herbs, often with succulent leaves and attractive flowers. Many are grown in gardens, including **Rock-moss,** *Portulaca grandiflora* [coloured plate VIIIb], from Brazil and *Lewisia brachycalyx* [298] from the Rocky Mountains.

The 1,500 members of the **Pink** family, *Caryophyllaceae* [299–309], are mostly annual or perennial herbs with pairs of simple, entire, often narrow opposite leaves. The flowers are usually bisexual with five sepals, five free petals and 10 stamens. The fruit is a capsule which opens by apical teeth to release the numerous seeds.

The family is mainly north temperate but some species

are found in south temperate regions and on mountains in the tropics. It is of economic importance for the large number of ornamental species which are cultivated.

The **Greater Stitchwort**, *Stellaria holostea* [299], is a common perennial herb of hedgerows throughout the British Isles, Europe, North Africa and the Near East. It has weak ascending stems and stiff lanceolate leaves. The white flowers are about an inch across and have deeply bifid petals. The **Field Mouse-ear Chickweed**, *Cerastium arvense* [300], is widespread in the northern hemisphere. In Britain it is most prevalent in eastern districts on dry soils. It is similar to the **Greater Stitchwort** but the leaves are downy, the flowers are smaller and the ovary has five, not three, styles. The **Arctic Mouse-ear Chickweed**, *C. arcticum* [301], is a small variable species with elliptical leaves and white flowers which occurs in Scandinavia and on high mountains in Wales and Scotland.

The annual **Corn Cockle**, *Agrostemma githago* [302], probably originated in the Mediterranean area but it has become naturalized as a cornfield weed in most temperate regions. The seeds may be poisonous and affect the quality of flour but in Britain at least it is less common than it was formerly. It has an erect

301
302

303

305
306

stem, narrow leaves and solitary terminal flowers with long pointed sepals and reddish-purple petals.

The **White Campion**, *Silene alba* [303], is a widespread north temperate plant common throughout Britain in hedgerows and waste places. It is a hairy perennial with male and female flowers on separate plants. It is often attacked by a smut fungus which stimulates the development of stamens in female flowers but the anthers are filled with fungal spores instead of pollen grains. Pink-flowered hybrids between this species and the **Red Campion**, *S. dioica*, are frequent.

Minuartia striata [304] is a mat-forming perennial which grows among rocks in the sub-alpine zone of high European mountains. The **Moss Campion**, *Silene acaulis* [305], is a widespread arctic-alpine plant which occurs on mountain ledges around the world in northern latitudes. It is a perennial forming dense light green cushions. The flowers are deep pink.

The largest genus, *Dianthus*, is the source of our numerous garden **Pinks** and **Carnations.** It includes *D. praecox* [306] with fragrant white flowers which grows on calcareous rocks in the west Carpathians; the **Sweet William**, *D. barbatus* [307], a native of southern Europe; *D. superbus* [308] with pink or white, deeply cut petals which is also cultivated; and *D. glacialis* [309], a small tufted species which grows at alpine and sub-alpine levels in the eastern Alps and Carpathians.

307

309

308

310

The family *Plumbaginaceae*, which is centred in the Mediterranean and Near East areas, includes about 300 species of perennial herbs and shrubs. Many grow in maritime, dry or alpine situations and include the **Prickly Thrift**, *Acantholimon venustum* [310], the widespread **Thrift** or **Sea Pink**, *Armeria maritima* [311], and species of **Sea Lavender**, *Limonium* spp.

Many of the 1,400 species belonging to the **Goosefoot** family, *Chenopodiaceae*, are herbs or shrubs which live in dry or coastal areas. *Salicornia herbacea* [312], one of the **Glassworts**, grows on coastal mud flats which are covered by high tide. Various species of **Orache**, *Atriplex* spp., are common garden weeds. *A. nitens* [313] is a native of southern Europe.

311

312

313

314

The *Amaranthaceae* includes about 800 species most of which are tropical. The flowers are small and grouped into dense inflorescences. It is of little economic importance but some species are grown as ornamentals including the **Foxtail**, *Amaranthus caudatus* [314], and the **Cockscomb** [315], a cultivated variety, var. *cristata*, of the tropical *Celosia argentea*. They vary greatly in habit and include annual and perennial herbs, climbers and some trees.

The **Knotgrass** family, *Polygonaceae* [316–324], includes about 800 species, the majority of which occur in north temperate regions. They are mainly herbs or shrubs with simple alternate leaves. The small bisexual flowers have inconspicuous perianth parts which often become larger and persist around the single-seeded fruit. **Rhubarb** and **Buckwheat** belong to this family, but otherwise it is of minor economic importance. Some species are grown for ornament.

315

316

317

318

name, **Snakeroot**. It is scattered throughout most of Britain, Europe and central Asia. The flowers are usually pink and are borne in dense cylindrical clusters. In the English Lake District the leaves are eaten in Easter-ledge puddings.

P. viviparum [320] has a circumpolar arctic distribution and also occurs on mountains farther

319

The genus *Rumex* [316] includes the widespread **Docks** and **Sorrels**. They are wind-pollinated and hybrids are common. **Rhubarb**, *Rheum undulatum* [317, 318], which is commonly cultivated for its succulent leaf stalks, is a native of northern Mongolia and the Baikal region.
Polygonum is a widespread genus of some 200 species which has been divided into several genera by some botanists. **Bistort**, *P. bistorta* [319], is a perennial with a thick twisted rhizome, alluded to by its other common

320

south. It is a perennial with a long slender inflorescence only the upper part of which is occupied by small white flowers. The small purplish bulbils which replace the lower flowers are easily detached and act as organs of vegetative reproduction. *P. alpinum* [321] is also a mountain species widespread in Europe and Asia.

P. baldschuanicum [322] is a woody climber with ovate leaves from Bokhara. It is often grown in gardens, and sometimes escapes. Other large species which are commonly cultivated and found more or less naturalized are *P. polystachyum* from Assam and Sikkim and *P. cuspidatum* [323], a native from Japan.

Buckwheat, *Fagopyrum esculentum* [324], is probably a native of central Asia but it has been cultivated for a long time in many countries for green fodder and as a grain crop. It is an erect annual with loose clusters of flowers.

167

323
324

The *Casuarinaceae* is a small family of about 50 species all belonging to the genus *Casuarina*. They are evergreen trees or shrubs found mainly in Australia and Malaya. *C. equisetifolia* [325] has slender green branches and minute whorls of leaves which give it the appearance of a Horsetail. The minute flowers are unisexual and borne in slender catkins. The hard timber, often known as She-oak, is of commercial value.

325

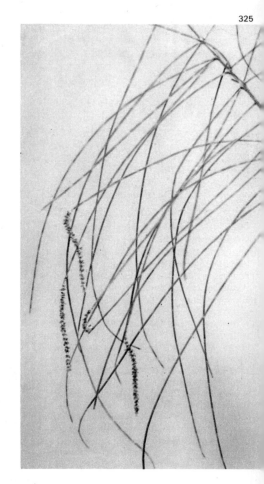

XI *Rosa foetida*

XIIa *Lupinus polyphyllus*

XIIb *Cotoneaster horizontalis*

326

The small but widespread family *Myricaceae* includes about 50 species most of which belong to the genus *Myrica*. They are trees or shrubs with alternate aromatic leaves and small unisexual flowers borne in catkins. The fruits of several species of American Bayberries, for example *M. caroliniensis* and *M. cerifera* [326], are covered with a thick layer of wax which is used to make candles. The **Bog Myrtle** or **Sweet Gale**, *M. gale*, is often abundant in wet places throughout the British Isles, Europe and North America.

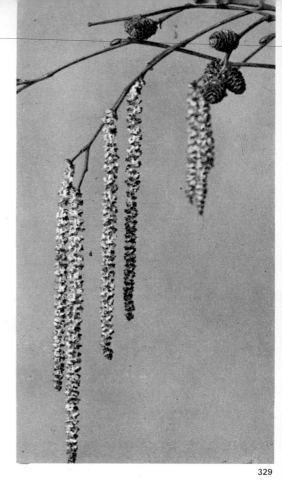

327
328

329

The distribution of the **Walnut** family, *Juglandaceae*, is mainly north temperate although extending to the tropics. It includes about 50 species, all with alternate pinnate leaves. They have small unisexual flowers which are wind-pollinated. The **Walnut**, *Juglans regia* [327, 328], is a native of south-eastern Europe and Asia but it has long been planted for its edible fruit and valuable timber and has become more or less naturalized in many countries including Britain. It reaches 100 feet in height and has a pale grey bark. The male flowers are borne in dense pendulous catkins [327]. The green fruit [328] has an outer leathery layer surrounding the familiar 'walnut'. **Black Walnut**, *J. nigra*, is an American tree which provides valuable wood and an esteemed nut. The American genus *Carya* includes a number of trees of considerable importance for both their wood and their fruits. Among these are the **Pecan**, *C. pecan*, the **Shellbark Hickory**, *C. ovata*, and the **Mockernut**, *C. alba* [330].

The **Birch** family, *Betulaceae*, includes about 70 species of north temperate deciduous trees. The minute male and female flowers are borne in separate catkins. The common **Alder**, *Alnus glutinosa* [329], is often abundant by lakes and rivers throughout much of the British Isles, Europe and Asia and naturalized in North America. The male catkins, which appear very early in the year, are long and narrow. When mature the female catkins resemble small black cones. The **Green Alder**, *A. viridis* [331], is a small shrub found at high levels in European mountains. The **Silver Birch**, *Betula pendula* [332], is a graceful tree common on heaths in Britain, Europe and western Asia. The erect female catkins are much smaller than the pendulous male catkins. *B. pubescens* [333] is a similar species which is able to grow in wetter and colder situations.

331

330

332

171

334

335
336

337

The **Hazel** family, *Corylaceae*, is often included in the closely related *Betulaceae* but the male flowers have a perianth and are inserted singly in the axil of each catkin bract. It includes about 50 species of north temperate deciduous trees. The **Hop Hornbeam**, *Ostrya carpinifolia* [334], is a native of southern Europe and Asia Minor. The mature fruits are enclosed in bracts on ovoid catkins. The wood of this species is very hard and is used for making mallets. The only other species, *O. virginiana*, the **Ironwood** or **American Hop-hornbeam**, is a native of North America. The **Common Hornbeam**, *Carpinus betulus* [337], is found throughout Europe and western Asia. It is also native in southern England but has been planted elsewhere. It is an attractive tree with a grey, characteristically grooved trunk. The ripe fruits are attached to large trilobed bracts. The **Hazel**, *Corylus avellana* [338], is common throughout the British Isles, Europe and Asia Minor. It produces its long male catkins and bud-like groups of female flowers very early in the year. The fruit is a woody nut surrounded by a thin toothed bract. American species are *C. cornuta* and *C. americana*.

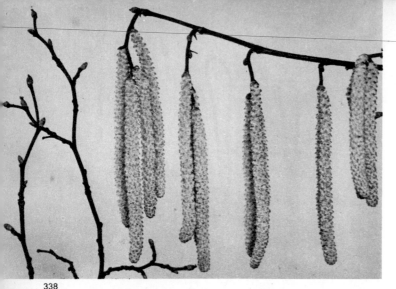

338

339

The **Beech** family, *Fagaceae*, is a large and important one of at least 600 species found mostly in temperate and subtropical parts of the northern hemisphere although one genus, *Passania*, is tropical and another, *Nothofagus*, is confined to the southern hemisphere. They are nearly all deciduous or evergreen trees with simple alternate leaves. The minute male flowers are usually crowded in slender catkins and the female flowers occur singly or in small groups. The fruit is a one-seeded nut which is surrounded by a capsule.

The family is of considerable economic value, mainly for the timber obtained from various species of **Oak**, *Quercus* spp., **Beech**, *Fagus* spp., and **Chestnut**, *Castanea* spp., but also for cork from the **Cork Oak**, *Quercus suber*, and several kinds of edible fruits.

The **Sweet** or **Spanish Chestnut**, *Castanea sativa* [335, 336], is a native of southern Europe, Asia Minor and the Caucasus which has been widely planted and is fully naturalized in south-east England. It is a tall tree with a dark brown, spirally grooved bark. The large oblong leaves have pointed marginal teeth. The long slender catkins bear many male flowers and a few female flowers at the base. From one to three large brown nuts are enclosed in a green spiny capsule which opens by several valves.

The **Beech**, *Fagus sylvatica* [339], is widespread in Europe and Asia. In Britain it is a true native in south-east England where it often forms fine woods on calcareous soils. It attains a height of over 100 feet and has a smooth pale grey bark. The male flowers are borne in dense heads on pendulous stalks. The fruit consists of one or two three-sided nuts enclosed in a four-valved scaly capsule.

3

There are over 500 species of **Oaks** of which the **Durmast** or **Sessile Oak**, *Quercus petraea* [342], and the **Common** or **Pedunculate Oak**, *Q. robur* [340, 341], are widespread in Britain, Europe and western Asia. In Britain the former is the usual dominant woodland tree on acid soils in the north and west of England but farther south the **Common Oak** is more abundant on heavy basic soils. The **Common Oak** has a broader crown and the edge of the leaf blade on either side of the stalk is reflexed. The male flowers [341] are borne in groups on pendulous stalks. The female flowers occur in small solitary groups which are stalked in the **Common Oak** and sessile in the **Durmast Oak**. The fruit [342] or acorn is a nut borne in a scaly cup. The **Turkey Oak**, *Q. cerris* [343], which has spiny cups, is a native of Europe and south-west Asia.

The greatest number of oaks is found in North America—perhaps 50 species. They include **White Oak**, *Q. alba*, and **Red Oak**, *Q. borealis*, valuable timber trees, and the common **Evergreen** or **Live Oak**, *Q. agrifolia*, of California, and *Q. virginiana* of the south-eastern United States. The **Willow Oak**, *Q. phellos* [344], with narrow leaves and small acorns grows mostly in the southern states.

342
343

344

346

347

348

The **Witch-hazel** family, *Hamamelidaceae*, is widespread but centred mainly in Asia. It includes trees or shrubs with simple alternate leaves, small flowers and two-celled woody fruits. The **Japanese Witch-hazel**, *Hamamelis japonica* [345], is a shrub up to 10 feet high which produces small flowers on the bare twigs in February. The yellow petals are very narrow and crumpled. In contrast *H. virginiana* [346], which is a larger shrub from eastern North America, bears its yellow flowers in October or November.

The six to eight species of **Plane** trees constitute the family *Platanaceae*. They all have a smooth bark which peels off in large flakes, alternate, palmately lobed leaves with axillary buds enclosed by the hollow leaf base, and unisexual flowers borne in dense spherical heads. The **London Plane**, *Platanus* × *hybrida* [347, 348], is a hybrid between the American **Button Wood** (in America, the **Sycamore**), *P. occidentalis*, and the **Oriental Plane**, *P. orientalis*, a native of southeast Europe. It originated about 200 years ago and has often been planted in towns.

179

349

350

The **Mulberry** family, *Moraceae* [349–355, 360], is a large one of over 1,000 species most of which are widespread in tropical and subtropical regions. They are nearly all trees or shrubs with simple alternate leaves and are distinguished from related families by the presence of a milky latex. The minute, crowded, unisexual flowers are often borne on a modified axis which becomes enlarged later to form a multiple fruit. The individual fruit formed from a single flower is one-seeded. The family is important economically for the many edible fruits such as **Mulberries**, *Morus* spp., **Bread-fruit** and **Jack-fruit**, *Artocarpus* spp., and **Figs**, *Ficus* spp.

The **White Mulberry**, *Morus alba* [349], is a native of China, but has been cultivated for many years in other parts of Asia and in the Mediterranean area because its leaves are the best source of food for silk-worms. It is a spreading tree up to 50 feet in height with big, light green, heart-shaped leaves. The small flowers are borne in short pendulous catkins. After fertilization the perianths of the female flowers become fleshy and coalesce, forming the logan-berry-like white or pinkish 'fruit'. The **Black Mulberry**, *M. nigra* [350], is a smaller tree which has also been cultivated in Europe and Asia for many centuries. The leaves are dark green above and hairy below. The fruit is similar to that of the **White Mulberry**, but dark red. The so-called **Red Mulberry**, *M. rubra*, is an American species with purple fruits.

The **Osage-orange**, *Maclura pomifera* [351, 352], is a native of the eastern United States where it is often known as **Bow-wood** because its silky yellow wood was used for bows by the Osage tribe of Indians, also as **Hedge** from its usefulness along boundaries. It is a deciduous tree up to 50 feet high with spiny branches and lanceolate entire leaves. The small greenish male and female flowers are borne in stalked spherical clusters on separate trees. After fertilization the whole female head swells up to form the rough, greenish-yellow fleshy fruit which is about four inches across [352]. This tree is sometimes grown in European gardens for its ornamental value.

351
352

The **Common Fig**, *Ficus carica* [353, 354], probably originated in western Asia but it has been cultivated from earliest times in the Mediterranean region, and is now extensively grown in California. It is also grown in Britain, mainly as an ornamental, but in favourable situations fruit is produced although pollination is not involved. It is a deciduous shrub or small tree with long-stalked, palmately lobed leaves up to eight inches long. The minute flowers are borne on the inner surface of a hollow pear-shaped receptacle which has a small terminal opening. The male and female flowers are produced in separate receptacles on the same tree. Pollination of the most-used varieties is effected by a gall-wasp which lays its eggs in the female receptacle. This then enlarges to form the fleshy fig containing the one-seeded fruits.

There are from 700 to 800 species of *Ficus*, most of which are tropical. Many are epiphytes which grow on other plants. The best known is the **Banyan**, *F. bengalensis*, which soon kills its host tree and sends down numerous supporting aerial roots. The well-known

353

354

Indiarubber Plant, *F. elastica,* forms a very large tree in the forests of India and Malaya.

Most of the 150 species of *Dorstenia* are natives of the tropical areas of Africa and America. They are unusual in being herbaceous, e.g. *D. radiata* [355]. The unisexual flowers are minute, the male consisting of a single stamen with a very short stalk, and the female represented by a simple ovary with a single style and bifid stigma. The flowers are borne in separate pits on the upper surface of a thick circular receptacle. This is borne on a long stalk and often has marginal extensions so that the whole complex inflorescence resembles a single flower. *Dorstenia* spp. are of no economic value but several are cultivated as ornamentals.

The **Paper Mulberry,** *Broussonetia papyrifera* [360], is a native of China and Japan. It is a small tree with very characteristically lobed leaves which are covered with woolly hairs on the undersurface. The flowers are borne in long pendulous catkins. The bark was formerly used for making paper in Japan.

355

356

183

357

The **Elm** family, *Ulmaceae*, is widespread in the northern hemisphere and consists of about 150 species of trees. They have alternate simple leaves which are often asymmetrical at the base of the blade. The flowers are small, unisexual or bisexual and borne in dense clusters. The one-seeded fruit is usually dry, flattened and winged. The main economic importance of the family is for the timber of various elms; some species of **Nettle-trees**, *Celtis* spp., yield edible fruits. There are from 20 to 30 species of **Elms**, *Ulmus* spp., occurring in north temperate areas and mountainous regions of tropical Asia. The **European White Elm**,

U. laevis [356, 357], occurs from central Europe to western Asia. The flowers are borne in clusters and have slender drooping stalks. The elliptical fruits each have a single seed in the centre. Leaf size, form and hairiness are important characteristics used to distinguish the various species of elm but they are extremely variable even on a single tree. Other species are the **Wych Elm**, *U. glabra*, with large, rough leaves, a native of Britain, Europe and western Asia; and the **English Elm**, *U. procera*, which is apparently unknown outside Britain. *Zelkova serrata* [358] with pointed, serrated leaves and wingless fruits comes from Japan.

358

Most of the 500 species belonging to the **Nettle** family, *Urticaceae* [359, 361, 362], are herbs although a few are small shrubs or trees. They are predominantly tropical or subtropical with South America as the main centre. The leaves are simple and the minute green unisexual flowers are crowded on long or short axes. The fruit is small and one-seeded. Some genera have characteristic stinging hairs. The most important member economically is *Boehmeria nivea* from which Ramie fibre is obtained.

360

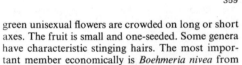

361

362

The all too familiar **Stinging Nettle**, *Urtica dioica* [359], which occurs throughout temperate regions, is a vigorous creeping perennial with erect angled stems up to five feet high and opposite pairs of toothed leaves. All the aerial parts of the plant are covered with stinging hairs although very occasionally they are absent. As its specific name indicates it is dioecious with the male and female flowers on separate plants. The female flowers are borne on long slender inflorescences. The **Roman Nettle**, *U. pilulifera* [361], is a native of southern Europe. It is an annual or biennial, both male and female flowers occur on the same plant and the female flowers are borne in spherical heads.

Laportea gigas [362] is a native of Queensland, Australia. It is a tree with poisonous stinging hairs and pink heads of fruits resembling raspberries.

The few species belonging to the family *Cannabinaceae* are sometimes included in the *Moraceae* (p. 180) but differ from other members of that family in the absence of milky latex. The **Hop**, *Humulus lupulus* [363], is a native of Britain, Europe and western Asia but is now cultivated in many temperate countries. It is a perennial twining climber which can reach a height of 20 feet. The small male flowers are borne on branched axillary inflorescences. The female flowers are produced on different plants in pendulous cone-like inflorescences which, when bearing fruit, are the 'hops' used in making beer. The characteristic flavour is due to lupulin which is secreted by glandular hairs present on the enlarged bracts.

187

The other member of the family of great economic importance is the **Hemp**, *Cannabis sativa* [364, male left, female right]. It is an erect annual with deeply palmate-lobed leaves. It originated in central Asia but has been cultivated for centuries in eastern countries for the narcotic resin it contains. Oil extracted from the seeds is also important and the fibres in the stem are separated and used to make string and cordage. Some varieties yield hashish and marijuana.

The **Laurel** family, *Lauraceae*, includes over 1,000 species of trees or shrubs, mostly natives of tropical south-east Asia. Many are evergreens with simple alternate leaves. The small flowers are usually bisexual and greenish, white or yellow. The one-seeded fruits are generally small and fleshy. The family is of economic importance for the aromatic oils present in the bark and foliage. **Cinnamon** is obtained from the bark of *Cinnamomum zeylanicum* [365] and *C. camphora* yields camphor. The **Bay** or true **Laurel**, *Laurus nobilis* [366], is probably a native of Asia Minor or south-east Asia but is plentiful in woods of the Mediterranean region.

364

365

366

367

The family *Calycanthaceae* contains only six species; three are natives of the southern United States, two occur in China and one is found in Queensland. They are shrubs with opposite, simple leaves and have flowers with many free parts.

The **Carolina Allspice** or **Carolina Shrub**, *Calycanthus floridus* [367], from the southern United States is often planted in gardens. The fragrant flower is about three inches across and has numerous strap-shaped dark red petals.

368

The members of the family *Hydrangeaceae*, which is often included in the *Saxifragaceae* (p. 197), are all trees or shrubs with opposite leaves. The flowers are bisexual, although some may be sterile, and the fruit is usually a capsule containing numerous seeds. The family is mainly north temperate but a few species occur in the tropics.

The commonly grown deciduous shrub known as **Syringa** or **Mock Orange** is *Philadelphus coronarius* [368], a native of south-east Europe and the Caucasus. The common name **Syringa** is liable to cause confusion because this is the scientific name for the **Lilacs** (p. 336) which belong to a different family. The beautiful white, strongly scented flowers are borne in

369

small terminal groups. Several
varieties are cultivated including
one with double flowers. There
are about 50 species of *Philadelphus*, mostly natives of the Far
East or North America, and many
of these are grown in gardens.
Hydrangea macrophylla [369] is a
native of China. It is a deciduous
shrub up to 15 feet high with
large, coarsely-toothed, bright
green leaves. The flowers are
crowded in a flattened head,
those at the periphery being
sterile and having large coloured
sepals. Most of our **Garden
Hydrangeas** [371] are derived
from this species but in these all
the pink, white and blue flowers
are sterile. They are propagated
mainly by cuttings. A number of
other species are also cultivated.
The genus *Deutzia* contains about
70 species of which *D. scabra* [370]
is one of the most popular. It has
finely toothed leaves and erect
groups of white or pinkish flowers.

191

372

373

374

The **Gooseberry** family, *Grossulariaceae* [372–376], consists of about 150 species of the genus *Ribes* often included in the *Saxifragaceae* (p. 197). They are widespread in the north temperate areas and also occur on the mountains of Central and South America. They are all shrubs with alternate, simple, often palmately lobed leaves. Usually the flowers are not very big and have petals which are smaller than the sepals. The ovary is below the level of the other floral parts and after fertilization it becomes a fleshy berry.

The **Gooseberry**, *Ribes uva-crispa* [372, 374], is widespread in Europe and parts of North Africa and is generally distributed in Britain. It is found in hedgerows and woods but some plants are escapes from cultivation. It is a deciduous shrub up to three feet high with spiny twigs and ovate, lobed leaves about two inches long. The small pale greenish flowers appear in small axillary clusters during April. The ovoid greenish bristly berry is about an inch long. It is frequently grown for the fruit and numerous cultivated varieties have been developed with larger yellow or red berries.

The **Red Currant** which is generally cultivated is *R. sylvestre* [373, 375]. It is a deciduous shrub up to six feet high with lobed, deeply cordate leaves about two inches long. The small yellowish-green flowers are borne in elongated pendulous groups. The fruits are about $\frac{1}{3}$ inch across, usually red but occasionally white. It is generally distributed in Britain and western Europe in woods, hedges and by streams. The exact status of this plant is uncertain; it may have originated in cultivation and subsequently become naturalized in suitable habitats. The closely related *R. spicatum* has larger, less cordate leaves. It occurs in northern Europe and Asia and is found in woods on limestone in Scotland and northern England. Both these plants are included in the 'aggregate' species *R. rubrum*. Hybrids between them are known and are the origin of some of our cultivated varieties.

The **Golden Currant**, *R. aureum* [376], is a native of North America which is sometimes grown in gardens. It has bright yellow fragrant flowers and dark purple fruits. The commonly grown **Flowering Currant**, which produces a mass of pink flowers in the spring, is *R. sanguineum*.

375

376

193

 377
378

379

The **Crassula** family, *Crassulaceae* [377–386], includes a large number of annual or perennial herbs with simple, more or less succulent leaves. The flowers have from three to 30 sepals and the same number of stamens and carpels. The latter are free or slightly fused at the base and give rise to a group of follicles when in fruit. It is widespread in dry, warm temperate regions except Australia and South America. Although their limits are not clear there are probably about 30 genera and 1,200 species. The family is of no economic importance except for the numerous species grown as ornamentals.

Crassula lactea [377] is a native of South Africa with white flowers. *Jovibarba hirta* [378] occurs mainly on the mountains of central Europe and the northern part of the Balkans. It is a perennial with open basal rosettes of dark green lanceolate leaves. The erect stem bears a terminal cluster of bell-shaped flowers with erect pale yellow petals. *Cotyledon retusa* [379] is a species with red flowers which comes from Mexico. *Crassula columella* [380] has short internodes so that the fleshy leaves form a thick erect column.

Cotyledon undulata [381] from South Africa is a shrubby species with beautiful leaves which have wavy edges and are covered with a white mealy deposit. The flowers are cream-coloured with a red stripe.

Sempervivum montanum [382] occurs in non-calcareous rocky situations on the mountains of southern Europe. It is a perennial which can reproduce vegetatively by means of slender stolons. The

380

381

narrow pointed leaves of the basal rosette are very
fleshy and sticky. The erect stems are about six inches
high and bear about eight dull red or, rarely, yellow

flowers. It is a variable plant and several subspecies
have been described based upon size and colouring
of the rosette.

382

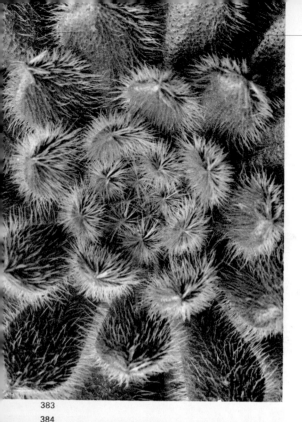

Echeveria setosa [383] is a species from Mexico which is often grown on rockeries. It has rosette leaves covered with long white hairs and orange flowers.

Sedum hispanicum [384] is usually an annual which occurs on the mountains of south-east Europe. It has small narrow glaucous leaves and the white star-like flowers are borne on one side of each erect stem.

Rhodiola kirilowii [385] is a species from northern China and central Asia which has separate male and female plants.

The **Garden Orpine** or **Live-forever**, *Sedum telephium* [386], is widespread in woods throughout the north temperate zone including the British Isles. It is an extremely variable perennial with tuberous roots, oblong fleshy leaves and dense terminal clusters of flowers which are often reddish-purple, though in the form illustrated, subsp. *maximum* from eastern Europe, the flowers are pale yellow.

383

384

385

387

The **Saxifrage** family, *Saxifragaceae* [387–389, 391], includes some 500 species of herbaceous perennials which are widely distributed in temperate regions. They are distinguished from the *Rosaceae* by the presence of two carpels which are usually partially sunk in the floral receptacle, and the capsular fruit.

386

388

389

390

391

198

The largest genus, *Saxifraga*, contains at least 300 species. *S. paniculata* [387] occurs on mountains throughout central and southern Europe. It possesses hemispherical rosettes of oblong, finely serrated, glaucous leaves which are often encrusted with lime. The erect stems are from four to 12 inches long and bear small terminal clusters of whitish flowers. This species is very variable in leaf shape and size. Many species and hybrids are grown in rock gardens, including *S. assimilis* [388] a new white-flowered hybrid.

The genus *Astilbe* includes about 20 species found in Asia and North America. They are popular herbaceous perennials for the garden and there are many cultivated hybrids and varieties. *A. davidi* [389] is a tall species with spikes of small crowded crimson flowers up to two feet long.

Bergenia crassifolia [391] from Siberia is a perennial with long thick leaves and erect clusters of large red flowers. This and other species are often grown for their early showy flowers.

The **Umbrella Plant**, *Peltiphyllum peltatum* [coloured

392

393
394

plate IXa], is a native of California which is frequently found in wet positions. It has large, toothed leaves and dense heads of small white or pink flowers on erect stems.

The Sundew family, *Droseraceae*, includes about 100 species of small perennial herbs. They are widespread in temperate and tropical regions and are often found on wet acid soils. A typical example of the main genus *Drosera* is the **Round-leaved Sundew**, *D. rotundifolia* [390]. It is common over most of the north temperate zone and is found throughout the British Isles on wet heaths and moors. It has a small basal rosette of leaves which have long stalks and circular blades [392] covered with slender glandular hairs. Insects are attracted by the leaves and get caught on the sticky hairs. The struggling insect stimulates the hairs to bend over and when it dies they secrete a digestive juice which breaks down the soft parts of its body. The soluble products thus formed are absorbed and utilized by the plant. The small white flowers are produced on one side of a long thin stalk which uncurls from the centre of the rosette.

199

395

396

The **Rose** family, *Rosaceae* [393–441, coloured plates X, XI], which includes over 2,000 species of herbs, shrubs and trees, is widely distributed especially in temperate regions. The leaves are nearly always alternate and have stipules. The bisexual flowers have numerous stamens and the ovary is more or less depressed in the receptacle. The fruits are of various kinds and often fleshy.

This large diverse family is of great economic importance for the valuable fruit-bearing species and also for the many ornamental shrubs and trees.

The genus *Spiraea* includes about 80 species of north temperate deciduous shrubs with simple leaves. Many are grown in gardens including *S. vanhouttei* [393] from China which produces dense clusters of small white flowers in May and June. *S. japonica* [395], a Japanese species, has larger leaves and bears its large flat clusters of red flowers later in the season. **Goat's Beard**, *Aruncus sylvester* [394, 397], is a handsome perennial with pinnate leaves and plumes of small pale cream flowers. It is often found beside streams and is best grown in moist and somewhat shaded positions.

Exochorda korolkowii [396] is a deciduous shrub from Turkestan. It reaches 15 feet in height and has simple obovate leaves and white flowers more than an inch across.

XIII *Dahlia pinnata*

XIV *Hibiscus syriacus*

398

399

White Kerria, *Rhodotypos kerrioides* [398], from China and Japan is a deciduous shrub with white flowers about two inches across. The fruit consists of four black, spherical parts each containing a single seed.

Kerria japonica [399] is a deciduous shrub from China with alternate leaves and solitary yellow flowers. A double form, var. *pleniflora*, is frequently seen in gardens.

The **Raspberry**, *Rubus idaeus* [400, 401, coloured

400

401

402

plate Xb], is common in the north temperate zone and occurs in woods and heaths throughout Britain. It is a prickly deciduous shrub with composite leaves. The white flowers are borne in small clusters and the familiar red fruit is a group of fleshy one-seeded drupelets.

The **Blackberry**, *R. fruticosus* [402], is a common prickly shrub throughout Europe and the British Isles. It is an extremely variable 'aggregate' species of which several hundred kinds have been described. In contrast, the **Cloudberry**, *R. chamaemorus* [403], has a creeping rhizome which produces annual aerial stems bearing palmately lobed leaves and no prickles. The solitary flowers are white and the orange-coloured fruit consists of a few drupelets. It occurs in north Europe, Asia and North America and is found on bogs in mountainous parts of Britain.

The **Shrubby Cinquefoil**, *Potentilla fruticosa* [404], has compound leaves and yellow flowers about an inch across. It grows on wet stony ground, often on mountains, and occurs widely in the north temperate zone including Britain where, however, it is rare.

The genus *Geum* includes the common woodland plant **Herb Bennet**, *G. urbanum*, and a number of attractive cultivated forms such as the red *G.* × *borisii* [coloured plate Xa].

The **Silverweed**, *Potentilla anserina* [405], is found throughout the north temperate zone and is common in rough pastures over the whole of the British Isles. It is a low creeping perennial herb with pinnate leaves, the toothed leaflets of which are covered with silky hairs. The solitary, axillary, yellow flowers are about an inch across. The fruit is a group of smooth, one-seeded achenes. *P. arenaria* [406] occurs on warm stony slopes from Sweden through central Europe to the Black Sea. The palmately lobed leaves are covered with star-shaped hairs. The flowers are deep yellow and appear as early as March. The **Wild** or **Woodland Strawberry**, *Fragaria vesca* [407, 408], occurs in woods and thickets on non-acid soils in Europe, western Asia and eastern North America. It has a perennial rootstock and toothed trifoliate leaves. The white flowers are similar to those of the **Silverweed** but smaller and the receptacle, which becomes fleshy in the fruit, bears the achenes on its surface. This is the parent of the **Alpine**

405
406

407

408

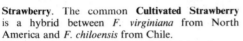

Strawberry. The common **Cultivated Strawberry** is a hybrid between *F. virginiana* from North America and *F. chiloensis* from Chile.

Mountain Avens, *Dryas octopetala* [409], is a circumpolar arctic-alpine species which occurs locally on mountains in the British Isles. It is a low perennial evergreen shrub with dark green oblong leaves. The solitary, axillary, white flowers are up to 1½ inches across. The fruit is a dry head of achenes with long persistent feathery styles.

Meadow-sweet, *Filipendula ulmaria* [410], is widespread in Europe and Asia and is common throughout the British Isles in marshes, fens and other wet places except where the soil is very acid. It is an erect perennial with toothed pinnate leaves. The small creamy-white flowers are strongly scented and are borne in crowded irregular clusters from June to September. The fruit consists of from six to 10 elongated achenes which become twisted around one another.

409

410

411

412

Alchemilla vulgaris, **Lady's Mantle** [411], is a variable 'aggregate' species which has been divided into a number of species based mainly on leaf form and distribution of hairs. It occurs in Europe, Asia and eastern North America and is common on wet grassland in the north and west of Britain. It is a small perennial herb with palmately lobed leaves which are often fringed with water drops in the morning. The minute green flowers have no petals and are borne in dense clusters. The fruit is a single achene.

There are at least 100 species of **Roses**, *Rosa* spp., which occur in north temperate and subtropical areas.

The **Romanus Rose**, *Rosa rugosa* [412], comes from northern China and Japan. It has thick, very prickly stems and the ovate dark green leaflets are hairy on the undersurface. The pinkish-purple flowers are about three inches across and very strongly scented. The large fruit is light red. This rose is often grown and used as a stock on which other species are grafted.

The **Dog Rose**, *R. canina* [413], grows in woods and hedges in Europe and south-west Asia and is the commonest species in England and Wales. It has strongly curved prickles and smooth serrated leaflets. The fragrant white or pinkish flowers are over an inch across and the ovoid fruits are scarlet. This is a very variable species and many varieties have been described.

414

Rosa tomentosa [414] has a distribution similar to that of the **Dog Rose**. It has stout prickles and the leaflets are usually hairy and glandular. The flowers are pink or white and the ovoid fruits are red. Other roses which are often cultivated include a small variety of the **China Rose**, *R. chinensis* var. *minima* [415], *R. xanthina* [417], a species from China with yellow flowers, and the so-called **Austrian Briar**, *R. foetida*

416

415

[coloured plate XI], from western Asia. Many garden varieties of roses [418] are complex hybrids which have been developed from a number of species over a long period of time. There are many American species, some used as parents of cultivated climbers. The **Cherry-laurel**, *Prunus laurocerasus* [416], a large evergreen shrub often planted in parks and gardens, is a native of eastern Europe and south-west Asia.

417

418

The **Gean** or **Wild Cherry**, *Prunus avium* [419], is a native of England and Wales and is also widespread in Europe and western Asia. It is a deciduous tree up to 60 feet high with a smooth reddish-brown bark. The alternate ovate leaves have serrate margins and two conspicuous glands at the top of the stalk. The

419

white long-stalked flowers appear in groups of from two to six in April or May. The succulent one-seeded fruits [420] are dark red and may be sweet or sour. The sweet garden cherries appear to be derived from this species. **Sour** and **Morello Cherries** are probably cultivated forms of *P. cerasus*.

420

422

The **Plum**, *Prunus domestica* [421], is a tree or shrub up to 20 feet high. The ovate leaves have serrate margins and are somewhat downy beneath. The white flowers occur singly or in groups of two or three and appear at the same time as the leaves unfold. The egg-shaped fleshy fruit is often bluish-black but may be red, yellow or green. It is doubtful if this tree occurs wild anywhere. It appears to be the result of hybridization, followed by further selection, between the **Cherry Plum**, *P. cerasifera*, and the **Blackthorn** or **Sloe**, *P. spinosa* [422, 423]. The latter is a deciduous shrub up to 15 feet high with many stiff blackish branches, some of which become short lateral thorns. The small white flowers are borne singly but close together on the bare branches before the leaves

421

423

424

425

unfold. The globose bluish-black fruit is about ½ inch long and contains a single seed within the hard central stone. This species is common in hedges and scrub throughout Britain, Europe and northern Asia.

The **Apricot**, *Prunus armenaica* [424], originated in northern China. It is a deciduous tree up to 30 feet high with a reddish bark and broadly ovate leaves. It has white or pink flowers about an inch across and the round fruit is yellow flushed with red. It has been planted since ancient times and there are many cultivated varieties.

The **Dwarf Russian Almond**, *Prunus nana* [425], is a small deciduous shrub about three feet high with toothed lanceolate leaves. The sessile red flowers are

about ½ inch across and the flattened dry ovoid fruit [426] has a velvety covering. *P. triloba* [427] is a deciduous shrub up to 15 feet high which comes from China. The broadly ovate, coarsely toothed leaves have long points and are often trilobed. The whitish-pink flowers are an inch across and appear in early spring. The small round hairy fruit is red.

The genus *Cotoneaster* includes about 50 species of deciduous shrubs mostly natives of China. Among the numerous species often cultivated is *C. multiflora* [428]. It reaches a height of 12 feet and has purplish slender drooping branches. The stiff ovate leaves are about two inches long. The flowers, which appear in small lateral clusters in May, have white spreading petals. The fruit is a small red berry. Another

426

427

attractive and frequently grown species is *Cotoneaster horizontalis* [coloured plate XIIb], a native of China with spreading, prostrate stems, pinkish flowers and globose bright red berries.

The **Medlar**, *Mespilus germanica* [429], is probably native of south-east Europe and Persia but owing to widespread cultivation it has become naturalized over the rest of Europe and southern England. It is a small tree or shrub up to 20 feet high and may bear thorns. The young twigs are hairy and the alternate, dull green lanceolate leaves are up to five inches long. The solitary terminal flowers are about two inches across and have pink or white petals. The brown globose fruit [430] is crowned with the persistent calyx and contains a single seed. At first it is hard and can be eaten only when the flesh has become over-ripe.

429

The **Hawthorns,** *Crataegus* spp., form a large genus in Europe and eastern North America. *Crataegus oxyacanthoides* [431] grows mostly in woods on heavy soils. It is found in Europe and also in Britain, especially in eastern areas. It is a small deciduous tree or shrub rarely more than 30 feet high and is armed with sharp thorns. The dark green shortly stalked leaves vary in shape; those on the short shoots have shallow toothed lobes whereas on the long shoots they are often more deeply lobed. The white flowers are borne in small clusters in late May. Most of the flowers have two styles and the ovoid dark red fruit has two stones. The **Common Hawthorn,** *C. monogyna*, is a very similar species but generally the leaves of the short shoots are more deeply cut, the flowers appear a little earlier and are borne in denser clusters. Most of the flowers have a single style and there is only one stone in the fruit. This species occurs throughout England and Europe, and where it grows with *C. oxyacanthoides* hybrids having intermediate characters are found. Pink, white and double varieties of both species, and of some American species, are often grown in gardens.

Quince, *Cydonia oblonga* [432], a native of central Asia, is a tree up to 20 feet high with woolly twigs and entire ovate leaves. The solitary white or pink flowers are two inches across. The pear-shaped fruit [434] is yellow when ripe.

430

431

XV   *Euphorbia pulcherrima* (**Poinsettia**)

XVIa *Chamaebuxus alpestris*

XVIb *Tropaeolum majus* (**Garden Nasturtium**)

The **Crab Apple**, *Malus sylvestris* [433], is a native of Europe and western Asia and is common in woods and hedges throughout the British Isles except the north of Scotland. It is a small deciduous shrub or tree up to 35 feet high with a fissured brownish-grey bark. The alternate dark green leaves are about two inches long and have oval, pointed, coarsely toothed blades. The flowers, which have pinkish spreading petals, are about two inches across and are borne in clusters on short spur shoots. The rounded fruits are rarely more than an inch in diameter. The skin is yellowish-green often tinged with red but the flesh is usually sour even when the fruit is ripe.

Two distinct subspecies are recognized. In subsp. *sylvestris* thorns are often present, the twigs are hairless and the small fruit is always sour. On subsp. *mitis* thorns are rarely found, the twigs are hairy and the large fruit is sometimes sweet. This form is a native of south-east Europe and south-west Asia and it appears to be the origin of most of our cultivated apples. Several crab apples are conspicuous trees in the North American flora.

Chaenomeles speciosa [435] is a native of China which is often grown in gardens and called the **Japanese Quince** or **Japonica**. It is a deciduous thorny shrub up to 10 feet high with smooth twigs and dark green, ovate, toothed leaves. The reddish flowers, which are about $1\frac{1}{2}$ inches long, are borne in small clusters on the old wood. The rounded fruit is up to two inches across with a greenish, speckled skin. Horticultural varieties with white, yellow or rose-pink flowers are sometimes planted.

433

434

435

The **Mountain Ash** or **Rowan**, *Sorbus aucuparia* [436], occurs throughout Europe and in western Asia as far as the Caucasus. In Britain it is commonest in the north and west where it grows at over 3,000 feet. It is an attractive deciduous tree up to 60 feet high with a smooth grey bark and hairy young twigs. The alternate pinnate leaves have from nine to 19 lanceolate, sharply toothed leaflets which are dark green above and rather glaucous below. The dense flat clusters of small creamy-white flowers appear during May and June. The globose fleshy fruits [437] are bright red and together with the yellow of the dying leaves make this a particularly attractive tree in the autumn.

438

439

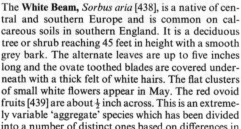

440

441

The **White Beam**, *Sorbus aria* [438], is a native of central and southern Europe and is common on calcareous soils in southern England. It is a deciduous tree or shrub reaching 45 feet in height with a smooth grey bark. The alternate leaves are up to five inches long and the ovate toothed blades are covered underneath with a thick felt of white hairs. The flat clusters of small white flowers appear in May. The red ovoid fruits [439] are about $\frac{1}{2}$ inch across. This is an extremely variable 'aggregate' species which has been divided into a number of distinct ones based on differences in leaf shape and habit. Hybrids between this species and both the **Mountain Ash** (p. 219) and the **Wild Service Tree**, *S. torminalis*, are known.

Some species of *Sorbus* have a very limited distribution. For example, *S. sudetica* [440] is confined to the subalpine zone of the Giant mountains. It is a small shrub about three feet high with pink flowers.

Amelanchier laevis [441] is a deciduous tree up to 30 feet high which comes from eastern North America. It has ovate, toothed leaves, slender groups of white flowers and sweet black berries.

442

The **Pea** family, *Leguminosae* [442–470], includes about 13,000 species. Most are temperate herbs but some are shrubs or trees and there are many representatives of the family in tropical and subtropical regions.

The **Mimosa** sub-family, *Mimosoideae* [442, 443], sometimes treated as a distinct family, *Mimosaceae*, comprises about 1,000 species of tropical and sub-

tropical herbs, shrubs and trees. The 350 species of *Mimosa* are mostly American herbs or small shrubs. *M. pudica* [442] is frequently cultivated in hothouses as a novelty. The bipinnate leaves are very sensitive and when touched fold up and droop. After a time the movements are slowly reversed. The 350 species of *Acacia* [443] are mostly trees. Typically they have bipinnate leaves but many that grow in Australia have

443

vertically flattened leaf stalks (phyllodes) and no leaflets. Many are of economic value including *A. senegal* which yields gum-arabic.

The **Judas Tree**, *Cercis siliquastrum* [444], is a member of the sub-family *Caesalpinioideae* which has also been treated as a separate family, *Caesalpiniaceae*. It is a small deciduous tree from the Mediterranean region with alternate, heart-shaped leaves. The clusters of reddish-purple flowers are produced directly on the bare woody branches. The fruit is a compressed red pod about five inches long.

The largest sub-family, the *Lotoideae* [445–470], sometimes raised to family status as the *Papilionaceae*, includes mostly temperate herbs. The typical papilionaceous flowers have 10 stamens and the fruit is a pod.

The **Pagoda Tree**, *Sophora japonica* [445], is a deciduous tree up to 80 feet high which is commonly planted in Japan although actually a native of China. It has pinnate leaves, groups of greenish-white flowers and constricted pods about three inches long.

446

448

447

The **Garden Lupin**, *Lupinus polyphyllus* [446, coloured plate XIIa], a native of North America, is a perennial herb with palmate leaves which have up to 16 lanceolate leaflets. The blue flowers are borne in dense erect spikes. This species is rarely seen in cultivation now, being replaced by the multi-coloured Russell lupins of hybrid origin. A large number of species of *Lupinus* are found in western North America.

Golden Rain, *Laburnum anagyroides* [447, 448], is a native of central and southern Europe but is widely cultivated and has become more or less naturalized elsewhere. It is a small tree with a smooth bark and alternate trifoliolate leaves. The golden-yellow flowers [448] are in pendulous groups and the flattened pods [447] each contain several poisonous seeds.

The **Spanish Broom**, *Spartium junceum* [449], which comes from southern Europe, is a shrub with cylindrical green rush-like stems and small narrow leaves. The yellow flowers are pleasantly scented.

The **Soya Bean**, *Glycine soja* [450], is a Japanese plant widely cultivated in eastern Asia for its valuable edible seeds. It is also used as a green fodder.

The **Common Broom**, *Sarothamnus scoparius* [451], occurs throughout Europe and the British Isles where it is found mainly on sandy soils of heaths and waste ground. It is a much-branched deciduous shrub about three feet high with erect, slender, five-angled, green stems and small leaves. The yellow flowers appear in May and June and are pollinated by bumble bees. The flattened black pods are about two inches long. A prostrate form, subsp. *maritimus*, grows on cliffs near the sea.

Wisteria sinensis [452] is a native of China. It is a woody climbing plant which is often grown against walls and on trellis work. The alternate pinnate leaves have ovate leaflets with wavy margins. The long pendulous racemes of lilac, or occasionally white, flowers are produced in great abundance in May and June. The flattened pods are about six inches long.

The **Coral Tree**, *Erythrina crista-galli* [453], comes from South America. It is up to five feet high and has trifoliolate, prickly leaves with ovate leaflets. The red flowers have large standard petals and appear in dense terminal racemes in July. It can survive out-of-doors during the summer but has to be brought inside for the winter.

The **False Acacia** or **Black Locust**, *Robinia pseudoacacia* [454], is a native of eastern North America, but it has been widely planted and is now more or less naturalized in other north temperate regions. It is a deciduous tree up to 80 feet high with twisted branches

452
453

226

and a dark grey, deeply grooved bark. The large leaf has elliptical leaflets and a sharp stipular spine on each side of the base. The pendulous clusters of fragrant white flowers appear in June. The dark brown pods which are formed later are about three inches long.

There are about 20 species of *Robinia*, all natives of North America. Amongst those sometimes planted for decorative purposes in Europe and Britain are *R. hispida*, the **Rose-acacia**, a small tree up to 12 feet high with hairy twigs and no spines, and *R. viscosa*, **Clammy Locust** [455], which has sticky twigs and inflorescence stalks.

Bladder Senna, *Colutea arborescens* [456, 457], is a deciduous shrub from the Mediterranean region. It attains a height of about 12 feet and has alternate pinnate leaves with obovate entire leaflets. The small racemes of yellowish flowers appear in June and July. The pods [457] are inflated and have thin papery walls. Its leaves are used to adulterate senna which is obtained from *Cassia* spp.

455

456

457

458

460
461

Arachis hypogaea [458, 461], the common **Peanut** or **Groundnut**, is a native of Brazil but is now widely cultivated in the warmer parts of North America, Africa and India. It is a small herb with shortly stalked yellow flowers. After fertilization the stalk of the ovary elongates and the young fruits are pushed underground where they ripen. The seeds of the mature fruits [458] are a valuable source of oil.

Oxytropis pilosa [459] grows in warm regions and *Astragalus penduliflorus* [460] is a rare **Milk Vetch** found on calcareous rocks in the Pyrenees, Alps and Carpathians. Very many species of *Astragalus* inhabit western North America, some being poisonous: these are called **Loco-weeds** since animals grazing on them act as if crazy ('loco').

459

229

There are nearly 300 species of **Clovers**, *Trifolium* spp., most of which are north temperate. *T. alpestre* [462] is found in Europe in dry woods and sunny situations. It is a perennial herb up to a foot high with spherical heads of purple flowers which appear between June and August. *T. montanum* [464] is another European species which occurs on slopes and in scrub particularly on calcareous soils. It is from eight to 15 inches high and bears heads of small white flowers between May and August.

The **Crown Vetch**, *Coronilla varia* [463], is a native of central and southern Europe which has become naturalized in a number of places in Britain and America. It is a poisonous perennial herb with heads of purple, pink or white flowers. The narrow pods break up into one-seeded portions.

Alfalfa or **Lucerne**, *Medicago sativa* [465], probably originated in western Asia and the Mediterranean region but is widely grown for green fodder and has become naturalized in many places. It is a perennial one to three feet tall with trifoliolate leaves. The dense clusters of purple flowers are pollinated by bees and the twisted pod contains up to 20 seeds.

The *Leguminosae* include many species of economic importance apart from those already mentioned. These include the ordinary **Garden Pea**, *Pisum sativum* [466, 467], which originated in the Mediterranean region. It has white flowers and cylindrical pods.

464
465

463

231

466

468

Sweet Pea, *Lathyrus odoratus* [468], an annual climber of many cultivated varieties, is also from the Mediterranean area. The **Broad Bean**, *Vicia faba* [469], is a native of south-western Europe which has been cultivated over a long period for its edible seeds. The **Runner Bean**, *Phaseolus vulgaris* [470], is a twining plant with scarlet flowers.

Plants of the *Leguminosae* have nodules on their roots containing bacteria which are able to utilize atmospheric nitrogen. Members of this family are therefore invaluable for improving nitrogen-deficient soils.

467

469

470

471

The **Tea** family, *Theaceae*, includes about 500 species of trees and shrubs many of which are tropical. The garden **Camellia**, *Camellia japonica* [471], is a native of Japan with large red flowers. The **Tea Plant**, *C. sinensis* [472], is widely cultivated in moist tropical regions.

The **Yellow Bird's-nest** or **Pinesap**, *Monotropa hypopitys* [473] belongs to the small north temperate family *Monotropaceae*. It is a non-green saprophytic herb which grows mainly in coniferous and beech woods. The yellow or pinkish waxy flowering stems appear in June and August.

472

473

The **Wintergreen** family, *Pyrolaceae*, is a small one of about 35 species which grow in arctic and north temperate regions. They are all perennial rhizomatous evergreen herbs. Although containing chlorophyll and capable of photosynthesis they are partial saprophytes found particularly on the undecayed humus of pine woods.

Pyrola rotundifolia [474], the **Larger Wintergreen** or **Shinleaf**, is scattered throughout the British Isles, Europe, northern Asia, Asia Minor and North America, and occurs in wet places such as bogs, fens, rock-ledges, duneslacks and damp woods. It has a slender creeping rhizome and all the glossy, dark green round leaves arise at ground level. The white flowers are borne in extended groups at the top of erect stems between July and September. The petals of the globose corolla are not fused together. The fruit is a capsule which contains many small seeds. The embryo within the seed is minute and undifferentiated. Two other similar widespread species are the **Common Wintergreen**, *P. minor*, and the **Intermediate Wintergreen**, *P. media*.

The **Heath** family, *Ericaceae* [475–492], is a large one of about 1,900 species which are widely distributed in temperate regions of both north and south hemispheres and on mountains in the tropics particularly on acid soils. They are mostly perennial shrubs or trees with simple entire leaves. The corolla often has a waxy texture and consists of joined petals. The fruit is usually a capsule or berry and contains numerous small seeds. Many species are found on acid soils and do not thrive on chalk or limestone.

474

475

The **Labrador Tea**, *Ledum palustre* [476], is an ever-green shrub up to three feet high which is widespread in northern parts of Europe and Asia and it is found also in a restricted area of Scotland. It has narrow dark green leaves and a dense terminal cluster of cream-coloured flowers which appear in June and July. The petals are not joined and the oblong capsule contains flat narrow seeds.

One of the most important groups in the family is the genus *Rhododendron* with at least 600 species. Most of these occur in eastern Asia but a few are found in Europe, western Asia and North America. They are shrubs or occasionally trees with conspicuous buds and large leaves. The conspicuous corolla is usually funnel-shaped and slightly asymmetrical. Many species, including those formerly put in the genus '*Azalea*', and numerous hybrids are widely cultivated. *R. kotschyi* [475], which has white flowers, is a native of the central Carpathians. Many of the large-flowered forms grown in gardens and parks [477] are hybrids between *R. catawbiense*, a native of the south-eastern United States with large clusters of purple flowers, and various species from Asia.

The **Rose des Alpes** or **Alpenrose**, *R. hirsutum* [478], is a small plant up to three feet high which occurs on calcareous rocks in the central and eastern European Alps. It has small, glossy green, lanceolate leaves. Both the stem and leaves are bristly. The red flowers are about half an inch across and are borne in terminal groups during June. *R. ferrugineum*, a similar species except that it has no bristles, is also called **Alpenrose**.

476

478

477

235

479
480

R. praecox [481] is an ever-green shrub about four feet high which produces an abundance of reddish-purple flowers in early spring. It is a hybrid between *R. dauricum*, a native of Manchuria, and *R. ciliatum*, which comes from the eastern Himalayas.

Enkianthus campanulatus [479], a native of Japan, is a shrub up to 20 feet high with whorls of ovate, finely toothed leaves. The small, bell-shaped, creamy-white flowers appear in pendulous clusters during May. The fruit is a capsule.

The **Marsh Andromeda**, *Andromeda polifolia* [480], has a northern circumpolar distri-bution and is found mostly in bogs and wet heaths. It is a low evergreen shrub with a creep-ing rhizome and narrow pointed leaves. The nodding, globose, pink flowers appear between May and September. The fruit is a spherical capsule which contains smooth oval seeds. A more common Am-erican species is **Bog-rosemary**, *A. glaucophylla*.

237

483

Pieris japonica [482] is a native of Japan grown in parks and gardens. It is an evergreen shrub up to 10 feet high with rough brown twigs. The smooth, broadly lanceolate leaves are about three inches long and tend to be crowded at the ends of the shoots. The small, white, pitcher-shaped flowers are borne in terminal pendulous racemes during March and April. The fruits [483] are spherical, dry capsules. There are about 10 species of *Pieris* and several of those from China and North America are also cultivated.

The genus *Leucothoe*, which is closely related to *Andromeda*, includes about 35 species widely distributed in Japan, the Himalayas, Madagascar and both North and South America. Some are deciduous but **Dog-hobble** or **Fetterbush**, *L. catesbaei* [484], is an evergreen shrub up to six feet high from the southeastern United States. It has slender arching stems and leathery, lanceolate, sharply toothed leaves about five inches long. The small, white, bell-shaped flowers are borne in dense axillary racemes during May. The fruit is a dry capsule.

485

Some members of the family *Ericaceae* are abundant on the acid soils of heaths and moors where they may form the dominant vegetation over considerable areas. One of these, **Ling**, *Calluna vulgaris* [485], is widespread in the British Isles, Europe and western Asia. It is an erect, branched, evergreen shrub with slender wiry stems up to three feet high. On the main stems the small narrow leaves are spaced out but on the short lateral branches they overlap. The flowers appear during August and September in the axils of the leaves on the uppermost stems. Both calyx and corolla are thin and petal-like and of the same pale purple colour. The fruit is a small capsule which contains few seeds.

486

There are nearly 500 species of **Heaths**, *Erica* spp., many of which are trees native in South Africa. *E. carnea* [486], a south European species, is a small shrub which produces its pale purple flowers in early spring. This species and many others, including the **Bell Heather,** *E. cinerea*, and **Cross-leaved Heather,** *E. tetralix*, are often cultivated.

The **Bilberry**, also knows as the **Whortleberry** and **Whimberry**, *Vaccinium myrtillus* [487], has a range similar to that of **Ling**. It grows in similar situations but is more tolerant of exposure and shade. It is a small creeping deciduous shrub with erect green stems up to two feet long and small, ovoid, pale green leaves. The pendulous, globular, pinkish-green flowers are borne singly in the axils of the upper leaves from April to June. After pollination, usually by bees, the round juicy bluish-black berry [488] develops.

487

488

489

490

Highbush Blueberry, *Vaccinium corymbosum* [489], is a native of North America. It is a shrub up to 15 feet high which is sometimes cultivated for its attractive flowers and large fruits. Many other species of *Vaccinium* occur in North America and yield hybrids valuable for their fruit.

491

492

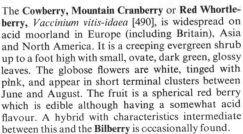

The **Cowberry, Mountain Cranberry** or **Red Whortle-berry**, *Vaccinium vitis-idaea* [490], is widespread on acid moorland in Europe (including Britain), Asia and North America. It is a creeping evergreen shrub up to a foot high with small, ovate, dark green, glossy leaves. The globose flowers are white, tinged with pink, and appear in short terminal clusters between June and August. The fruit is a spherical red berry which is edible although having a somewhat acid flavour. A hybrid with characteristics intermediate between this and the **Bilberry** is occasionally found.

The **Cranberry**, *Vaccinium oxycoccus* [491, 492], occurs in bogs and wet heaths. It has a geographical range similar to that of the **Cowberry** and is scattered over most of the British Isles. It is a small evergreen shrub with very thin prostrate stems which bear ovate green leaves about ¼ inch long. From one to four pink flowers [491] are borne at the end of each erect stem. The four petals are joined only at the base and curve away from the centre of the flower. The small red globose fruit [492] becomes edible only after exposure to frost.

493

The **Rockrose** family, *Cistaceae*, includes about 170 species, many of which are natives of the Mediterranean region. They are mostly shrubs or herbs with opposite leaves and bisexual flowers.

Helianthemum grandiflorum [493] is an evergreen trailing shrub found at high elevations in the Alps, Apennines and the Sudeten, Balkan and Caucasus mountains. It is closely related to the **Common**

494

495

Rockrose, *H. chamaecistus*, which occurs on basic grassland in Britain, Europe, western Asia and Asia Minor. The bright yellow flowers of the latter species are about an inch across and appear between June and September. There are numerous small sensitive stamens which bend inwards when touched. The fruit is an ovoid three-valved capsule.

There are about 19 species of *Cistus*, most of which are commonly cultivated. They differ from *Helianthemum* in being larger shrubs and having a five- or 10-valved capsule. *C. clusii* [494] is a native of North Africa which is grown in cool greenhouses.

The **Tamarisk** family, *Tamaricaceae* [495, 497], includes about 100 species of trees or shrubs which occur mainly in the Mediterranean area. *Tamarix gallica* [495] is a feathery deciduous shrub, three to 10 feet high, with tiny, glaucous, scale-like leaves and globose buds. The tiny bisexual pink or white flowers are borne in slender crowded spikes. The fruit is an ovoid capsule. This species and the very similar *T. anglica* with green leaves and ovoid buds occur in south-west Europe and have become naturalized on the southern and eastern coasts of England and in the south-western United States.

496

497

Myricaria germanica [497] is a rare European
species confined to the stony banks of mountain
streams. It is an evergreen shrub about eight feet
high with glaucous grey leaves. It produces dense
terminal racemes of small red or pink flowers
between June and August.

The **Storax** family, *Styracaceae* [496, 499], includes
about 120 species of shrubs and trees which are
widely distributed in the warmer parts of North and
South America, eastern Asia and the Mediterranean
region.

Styrax japonica [496] is a native of China and Japan.
It reaches a height of 25 feet and has alternate, ovate,
toothed leaves about three inches long. The beautiful
white flowers which hang downwards in small
clusters appear in June and July. A related species

498

499

from the Moluccas, *S. benzoin*, is the source of benzoin, a resin used in medicines.

The **Silver Bell Tree**, *Halesia carolina* [499], comes from the south-eastern United States. It is a deciduous tree up to 30 feet high with ovate, downy leaves. The clusters of pendulous white flowers appear on the old wood during May.

The family *Sapotaceae* includes about 600 species of tropical trees and shrubs with alternate, simple leaves and a milky or sticky latex. Several are of considerable economic importance, especially *Achras sapota* [498] which yields the chicle gum used in chewing-gum, and an edible fruit, the **Sapodilla Plum**.

500
501

The members of the **Willow** family, *Salicaceae*, are widespread mainly in north temperate regions. They are deciduous trees or shrubs with alternate, simple leaves. The small male [500] and female [501] flowers are borne in dense catkins on separate plants. There are no sepals or petals but each flower has a basal disk and one or two small nectaries. There are two or more stamens in the male flowers and each female flower has a one-celled ovary. The fruit is a capsule which opens by two valves to release the many minute, plumed seeds [502].

There are only two genera, *Salix*, the **Willows**, with about 300 species, mainly north temperate but a few arctic and tropical, and *Populus*, the **Poplars**, with some 30 species which are exclusively north temperate.

The **Willows** are trees or shrubs with the buds protected by a single scale. The flowers, which appear before or after the leaves unfold, are borne in the axils of entire scales on a catkin which is usually erect. Identification is often difficult because many species are extremely variable and hybridize freely. Further practical difficulties arise from the fact that the sexes are on separate plants.

A common species in wet places such as marshes and river banks is the **White Willow**, *S. alba* [501]. It is a graceful tree up to 90 feet high which is widespread in Britain, Europe and central Asia and in North Africa. The lower surfaces of the lanceolate, toothed leaves are covered with white silky hairs. There are several distinct varieties of this species including the **Cricket-bat Willow**, var. *coerulea,* with broader, bluish-green leaves, and the **Golden Willow**, var. *vitellina*, with bright yellow-orange stems.

Salix reticulata [504] is a small creeping shrub with dark green oval leaves. It is a circumpolar arctic species and is also found on mountains further south.

The **Poplars** are all trees with buds protected by several scales. The flowers are subtended by toothed scales and appear in pendulous catkins before the leaves unfold.

The **Black Poplar**, *P. nigra* [503], is common in wet places throughout Europe and western Asia. It attains a height of from 70 to 100 feet and has a black, deeply fissured bark. The **Lombardy Poplar**, var. *italica*, is a distinct variety.

The **Cottonwoods,** *Populus* spp., especially *P. deltoides*, are valuable trees along watercourses in the arid parts of western North America.

250

The **Viola** family, *Violaceae* [505–508], is a cosmopolitan family of some 800 species which may be trees, herbs or shrubs. Approximately half the members belong to the mainly temperate herbaceous genus *Viola*. The leaves are alternate and the flowers, which are usually borne singly, have bilaterally symmetrical corollas with the lower petal spurred. The fruit is a three-valved capsule.

Viola biflora [505] is found in wet stony places on mountains in Europe, Asia and North America and also in the Arctic. It has heart-shaped leaves and the bright yellow flowers which are usually borne in

axillary pairs appear in May and June. The **Wild Pansy**, *V. tricolor* [506], which has yellow or bluish flowers, is a small variable herb of cultivated land and pasture. It is widespread in the British Isles, Europe and Asia. A distinct subspecies of the **Mountain Pansy**, *V. lutea* subsp. *sudetica* [507], occurs on east European mountains as far as the Tatra range. The **Garden Pansy**, *V.* × *wittrockiana* [508], probably originated about 130 years ago from hybrids between *V. tricolor* and *V. lutea* subsp. *sudetica*. Many attractive species, such as *V. papilionacea*, **Birdfoot Violet**, *V. pedata*, and the yellow-flowered *V. pubescens*, appear in spring in North American woodlands.

506
507

509

The **Passion Flower,** *Passiflora coerulea* [509], is the
best-known member of the tropical American family,
Passifloraceae which includes about 600 species. It is a
climber with tendrils and palmately lobed leaves. The
large flowers have a complicated structure, one
striking feature being the central column or andro-
gynophore bearing the five stamens and the terminal
ovary with three styles.

510

The **Gourd** family, *Cucurbitaceae*, includes about 850 species most of which are tropical and subtropical herbs. They are prostrate or climbing vine-like plants with palmately lobed leaves and many possess tendrils. The flowers are unisexual and the sexes may occur on separate plants. The fruit, which is often large, is a berry containing many seeds.

Bryonia alba [510], although a native of southern Europe, has become naturalized farther north where it has been grown both for ornament and as a medicinal herb. It occurs in hedges where it clings to other plants by means of its strong tendrils. It has yellow-green flowers and the berries are black.

There are many cultivated varieties of *Cucurbita*

511

512

513

maxima [511, 512], but its natural origin is unknown. It is a coarse spreading annual with large fleshy fruits. In Europe they are known as **Pumpkins** and in the United States they are called **Squashes**. The American **Pumpkin** is *C. pepo* and it is the small hard fruits of var. *ovifera* of this species that provide ornamental **Gourds**.

The **Cucumber**, *Cucumis sativa* [513], is a native of southern Asia but there are many cultivated varieties. The **Squirting Cucumber**, *Ecballium elaterium* [514], grows in wet forests in the central and eastern Mediterranean regions. It is a rough annual with explosive fruits which can eject the hard seeds some 10 to 25 feet.

514

The **Begonia** family, *Begoniaceae*, includes about 800 species most of which are herbs from central and northern South America. Nearly all belong to the genus *Begonia*. They have alternate, simple leaves and the flowers are unisexual. They are extensively grown in greenhouses and there is a bewildering number of cultivated varieties and hybrids. Two of these are *B. ricinifolia* [515], which is a hybrid with lobed leaves, and *B. imperialis* [516], with hairy, variegated leaves.

515

516

517

The most important member of the small family *Caricaceae* is *Carica papaya* [517]. Although a native of tropical America it is now widely cultivated elsewhere in the tropics for its edible **Papaya** fruit. It is a rapidly growing, unbranched tree up to 20 feet high with large, palmately lobed leaves.

518

519

520

The **Campanula** family, *Campanulaceae* [518–526], includes about 700 species which have a cosmopolitan distribution. They are mostly herbs which contain a watery or milky latex. The alternate leaves are simple and the bisexual flowers are often showy. The fruit is usually a capsule containing numerous seeds. The family is of little importance economically except for the ornamental species which are widely cultivated. Most of the **Bellflowers**, *Campanula* spp., are found in north temperate regions or on tropical mountains. The flowers are markedly protandrous, i.e. the pollen is shed from the anthers well before the stigmas are exposed.

Campanula kladniana subsp. *polymorpha* [518] is confined to the Carpathians where it grows at alpine elevations.

The **Creeping** or **Rover Bellflower**, *C. rapunculoides* [519], is a native of Europe, western Asia and Asia Minor which has become widely distributed in the British Isles. It is a far-spreading perennial with ovate basal leaves and narrow stem leaves. The erect spikes of nodding, bell-shaped, bluish-purple flowers appear between July and September. The seeds are released from the hemispherical capsule through basal pores.

Campanula persicifolia [520] is widespread in Europe and Asia. It is often grown in gardens and has become naturalized in parts of southern England. It is a smooth perennial with small inflorescences of large, more or less erect, blue or white flowers.

258

521

522
523

Bats-in-the-Belfry or **Throatwort**, *C. trachelium* [521], is found in woods and hedges throughout Britain, Europe, Siberia and North Africa. It is a hairy perennial with simple, sharply angled stems up to three feet high. The large, bluish-purple flowers appear on branched inflorescences between July and September.
Campanula cochlearifolia [522] grows in wet places on stony slopes, especially where limestone is present, in the Pyrenees, Alps, Jura and Carpathians. It is a perennial with underground runners. The tufts of rounded leaves and erect stems form a dense mat four to six inches high. Between one and five drooping, bell-shaped, blue flowers are borne on each stem between June and September. Several varieties, including those with white and pale blue flowers are commonly grown in rock gardens.
Campanula alpina [523] is a rare plant confined to stony areas in the Carpathians and eastern Alps between 4,000 and 7,000 feet. It is a perennial with woolly stems up to nine inches high. Each bluish-lilac flower has a long curved stalk. Both this and a white-flowered variety can be easily cultivated.
The **Harebell**, *Campanula rotundifolia*, is found around the world in boreal regions and extends southward in mountain ranges.

524

The **Balloon Flower**, *Platy-
codon grandiflorum* [524], is a
native of China, Korea and
Japan. It is an erect perennial
up to two feet high with
smooth, toothed, lanceolate
leaves. When the terminal,
inflated flower-bud opens the
shallow blue corolla reaches
three inches in diameter. The
fruit is a capsule which opens
at the top. There are numerous
attractive varieties of this
species in cultivation.

Phyteuma spicatum [525] is a
native of central and southern
Europe, found also in a
restricted area of southern
England. It is a perennial
with a swollen, fleshy root and
rounded basal leaves. The inflorescence is a dense cylindrical head consisting of
yellowish-white flowers. The
fruit is an ovoid capsule. This
and many other *Phyteuma*
spp. are grown in herbaceous
borders and rock gardens. 525

526

Wahlenbergia pumilio [526] is a tufted perennial from Dalmatia which is sometimes planted in rock gardens. It has linear leaves little more than ½ inch long. Several erect bell-shaped, bright blue flowers are borne on each stem in May and June. The fruit is a capsule which opens by several apical valves.

528

The *Compositae* [527–602], sometimes known as the *Asteraceae*, is the largest family of flowering plants with at least 900 genera and 14,000 species. They are world-wide in distribution and are found in every type of habitat from mountain tops to the sea shore. Many are trees or shrubs but the majority are herbs. These may be annual or perennial and exhibit a wide range of leaf form and types of stems. However, there is a notable uniformity in inflorescence and floral structure. The flowers or florets are small and borne in a dense head or capitulum surrounded by an involucre of bracts. The florets are unisexual or

529

bisexual. When stamens are present they are attached to the corolla tube and the five anthers are joined together forming a cylinder around the style. The ovary is below the other floral parts and gives rise to a one-seeded fruit or cypsela which is often crowned with a pappus of hairs or teeth. The family is of economic importance for such food plants as lettuce,

artichoke and chicory and for a large number of valuable garden plants.

Hemp Agrimony, *Eupatorium cannabinum* [527], is a perennial herb up to four feet high which grows in wet places throughout the British Isles, Europe and Asia. It has lanceolate, opposite leaves and the dense clusters of small pinkish capitula appear between

265

530
531

266

July and September. Many familiar species of *Eupatorium*, including the **Joe Pye Weeds,** grow in North America.

The **Spike Gayfeather, Button-Snakeroot** or **Blazing-Star**, *Liatris spicata* [528], is a native of the eastern and southern United States. It attains a height of three feet and produces its handsome spikes of reddish-purple flowers in September.

Townsendia wilcoxiana [529], which grows high up on plains and hills from Oklahoma to Colorado, is a small plant with simple leaves and large yellow capitula.

The **European Goldenrod**, *Solidago virgaurea* [530], is a variable perennial which grows in dry places throughout most of the north temperate zone. It is from two to 30 inches high with broadly lanceolate leaves and loose terminal clusters of yellow capitula which appear between July and September. The **Goldenrod**, or a variety of it commonly grown in gardens is *S. canadensis* [531].

Bellis perennis [532], the **Daisy**, is abundant in short grassland throughout the British Isles, Europe and Asia. It has rosettes of spatulate leaves and solitary capitula with peripheral white female ray florets and central yellow bisexual florets.

Aster alpinus [533, coloured plate XXb] is widespread in stony pastures and among limestone rocks on the mountains of Europe and western Asia. It is a hairy perennial from two to six inches high. The solitary capitula which appear in July and August have mauve ray florets and yellow disc florets.

532

533

267

534

Aster bellidiastrum [534] grows in damp shady places on limestone rocks of the central European moun-

tains. It is a perennial with a basal rosette of coarsely toothed leaves. The solitary capitulum, which appears between April and September, terminating an erect stem from four to 14 inches long, has a marginal row of white ray florets surrounding numerous yellow disc florets. *Aster salignus* [535] is a North American plant which has become naturalized in Britain and Europe. It is a perennial up to six feet high with narrow leaves and large terminal clusters of capitula produced between July and September. The disc florets are yellow and the ray florets, white at first, turn bluish-purple. Some of the many other North American Asters are the ancestors of the Michaelmas daisies of the garden. *Baccharis trinervis* [536] is a native of tropical South America with ribbon-like stems and small capitula of white florets.

The **China Aster**, *Callistephus chinensis* [537], is an annual of which there are now a large number of cultivated varieties.

535

536

537

269

Cat's-foot, *Antennaria dioica* [538], grows in dry pastures, usually on calcareous soils in Britain, northern and central Europe, Siberia, the Caucasus and North America. It is a perennial with narrow woolly leaves and erect stems from two to eight inches high. The plants are unisexual, the terminal groups of male capitula usually being white and the female pink.

Edelweiss, *Leontopodium alpinum* [539], is widespread on the mountains of Europe and Asia. It has narrow woolly leaves and erect stems up to eight inches high. The terminal star-like flower has up to 15 radiating bracts and between three and eight small, circular, pale yellow capitula.

The many colourful varieties of the Garden Zinnia [540] are derived from the Mexican species *Zinnia elegans*. It is an annual from three inches to three feet high with ovate leaves and terminal capitula from two to five inches across.

The Everlasting Flower, *Helichrysum bracteatum* [541], a native of Australia, is an annual up to three feet high with large capitula having several rows of spreading, papery, persistent bracts. In the wild form the bracts are yellow, but there is a wide range of coloured varieties in cultivation.

538

539

540

542

543

544

Rudbeckia laciniata [542], the **Cone-flower**, is a native of North America. It is a perennial from two to seven feet high with lobed leaves. The large capitula produced during the summer have drooping yellow ray florets and a central conical group of greenish disc florets.

Common Sunflower, *Helianthus annuus* [543–545], is a native of the western United States. It is a stout hairy annual from three to 12 feet high with broadly ovate leaves up to a foot long. The terminal

545

capitulum produced between July and September [543], is up to a foot across, and even more in cultivation. It has several rows of involucral bracts [544] and a large number of yellow ray florets. The fruits [545] are used as a source of oil. Besides this annual species, North America has many perennials.

546

There are about 12 species of *Dahlia*, all natives of
Mexico and south-western United States. They are
erect perennials with opposite leaves and tuberous

roots. The thousands of cultivated varieties of
Garden Dahlias [546–548, coloured plate XIII] have
all been derived by selection and hybridization of

547

these species, particularly from the extremely variable *D. rosea*. However, all the **Cactus Dahlias** appear to have been derived from a single plant of *D. juarezii* which was introduced into Europe in 1864.

Yarrow, *Achillea millefolium* [549], is abundant in grassy and waste places throughout Britain, Europe and western Asia and has been introduced into North America, Australia and New Zealand. It has creeping underground stolons and erect green stems up to 18 inches high with pinnately dissected leaves. The small crowded capitula are produced between June and August. Each has five white ray florets and a few creamy disc florets.

Gaillardia pulchella [550] is a native of the south-western United States. It is a softly hairy annual from one to two feet high. The flat capitulum, about two inches across, has broad yellow ray florets which are usually reddish towards the base. Most of our annual **Garden Gaillardias** are derived from this species.

The so-called **African Marigold,** *Tageted erecta* [551], occurs wild in Mexico and south-western United States. It is an erect branched annual up to two feet high with pinnately divided leaves. In cultivation the rounded capitula vary greatly in size, and range in colour from pale yellow to deep orange. The small **French Marigold** is *T. patula*.

550

551

549

552
553

Santolina caespitosa [552] from western parts of the Mediterranean region is a small evergreen shrub with pinnatifid leaves covered with a thick felt of white hairs. The neat yellow capitula are borne on long stalks and lack ray florets.

Achillea schurii [553] occurs among wet rocks at alpine elevations in the east and south Carpathians. It has pinnately dissected leaves, and the capitula have white ray florets and yellow disc florets. The **Wild Chamomile**, *Matricaria recutita* or *M. chamomilla* [554], occurs abundantly in waste places on sandy soils in England and Wales. Europe and western Asia to India. It has also been introduced into North America and Australia. This is an erect, branched annual up to two feet high with alternate, finely dissected leaves. The numerous capitula which are produced in June and July have white female ray florets and many small bisexual yellow disc florets borne on a conical receptacle. This plant is strongly aromatic and Oil of Chamomile is extracted from its capitula, although in Britain the true chamomile is *Chamaemelum nobile*, and the American garden chamomile is *Anthemis nobilis*.

554

555

556

The **Scentless Mayweed**, *Tripleurospermum mariti-mum*, is widespread in the British Isles and temperate parts of Europe and Asia. It is a variable plant separated into two subspecies, subspecies *maritimum*, a prostrate, perennial with fleshy leaves, and sub-species *inodorum* [555], an erect annual usually with non-fleshy leaves. The latter, a common weed of cultivation with finely dissected leaves, attains a height of two feet. The capitula are an inch or more across and appear between July and September. Each has about 20 long white ray florets and numerous yellow disc florets.

The **Moon Daisy, Ox-eye Daisy** or **Marguerite**, *Chrysanthemum leucanthemum* [556], is a native of the British Isles, Europe and Asia and has been introduced into New Zealand and North America. A perennial with erect stems from one to two feet high and a basal rosette of spatulate leaves, it usually grows in grass-land or on roadsides. The capitula, which appear between June and August, are up to two inches across with numerous white ray florets and a central mass of yellow disc florets.

557

Chrysanthemum alpinum [557] is abundant on European mountains between 6,000 and 12,000 feet. It is a tufted perennial with pinnatifid leaves. The yellow and white capitula occur singly on erect stems from two to six inches high between July and September.

Tansy, *Chrysanthemum vulgare* or *Tanacetum vulgare* [558], is a perennial from one to four feet high which occurs in waste places in Britain, Europe and Asia. The leaves are deeply dissected and the clusters of capitula appear between July and September.

XVII *Jasminum nudiflorum*

XVIII *Daphne mezereum*

281

559

Most of our autumn-flowering garden **Chrysanthemums** [559] appear to have been derived from two species, *C. indicum* which has pinnatifid leaves and yellow capitula with short rays, and *C. morifolium* which has ovate leaves and capitula with white ray florets and yellow disc florets. They have been cultivated for centuries in the Far East and no doubt other wild species are involved in the production of our present-day varieties. Most of these are 'double' forms, all the florets in the capitulum being ligulate.

560

Wormwood, *Artemisia absinthium* [560], is widespread in the British Isles, temperate Europe and Asia and has been introduced into New Zealand and North and South America. It is a perennial from one to three feet high with dissected lower leaves and narrow, entire upper leaves. The numerous small globular capitula are borne on the upper stems in July and August. All the florets have yellow tubular corollas and are wind pollinated. It is a strongly aromatic plant and the oil extracted from it is used for flavouring absinthe. The genus *Artemisia* includes the **Sage Brush** of vast areas of western North America.

Coltsfoot, *Tussilago farfara* [561], is common throughout the British Isles and much of Europe and western Asia; it has also been introduced into North America. It is commonly found in large patches on clay soils and spreads extensively by means of white underground rhizomes. The solitary flowering heads appear before the leaves, in March and April, on slender stems covered with pinkish scales. The yellow capitulum is about an inch across with several rows of female ray florets and few male disc florets. The leaves appear in the summer; they have large rounded blades covered beneath with a thick felt of hairs.

Butterbur, *Petasites hybridus* [562, 563], occurs in wet places throughout the British Isles, Europe and western Asia and has been introduced into North America. It has a habit similar to that of Coltsfoot but the capitula are borne in dense clusters [562] between March and May. Owing to the partial sterility of the purplish florets the plants are practically unisexual. The one-seeded fruits have a pappus of whitish hairs [563].

Doronicum clusii [564] grows in rocky places on the Spanish mountains and in the Alps and Carpathians. It is a hairy perennial with a thick rootstock and narrow leaves. The solitary, terminal, bright yellow capitula are borne on erect, unbranched stems up to a foot high between July and September. Each is about two inches across with a single row of marginal ray florets and numerous disc florets.

Doronicum austriacum [565] is found in subalpine woods on European mountains. It is a somewhat hairy perennial growing to over two feet high with toothed leaves, the lower heart-shaped and upper ovate. Between one and five large yellow capitula are borne on each erect stem during the spring.

563
564

565

566

The **Mountain Tobacco** or **Mountain Snuff**, *Arnica montana* [566], grows in meadows and pastures on European mountains. It is an aromatic perennial with a creeping underground rhizome and oblong-lanceolate basal leaves. The erect stems are about a foot high and in July bear up to four yellow capitula about two inches across, with numerous ray florets and a compact centre of disc florets. Both the rhizomes and flowering heads have at times been used medicinally.

567

568

Doronicum cordatum [567] occurs in the mountains of south-eastern Europe and western Asia. It is a small perennial about five inches high with a thick mass of fibrous roots and kidney-shaped leaves. The stalked yellow capitula are produced in the spring.

The large genus *Senecio* [568–572] includes over 2,000 species. They are world-wide in distribution but most occur in the Mediterranean region and South Africa. The range of habit is great, from small annual herbs to succulents and trees.

Senecio vernalis [568], originally a native of southern Europe, is now distributed over much of Europe, North Africa and south-west Asia as a weed of cultivation. It reaches a height of nearly two feet and produces terminal clusters of yellow capitula between July and October.

The popular florists' **Cineraria** [569] is believed to have been derived from *Senecio cruentus* which was first introduced from the Canary Isles towards the end of the 18th century. It is a somewhat woolly perennial from two to three feet high; the large leaves have long stalks and heart-shaped blades. The

569

large flat-topped clusters of capitula are reddish-purple in the original form but continuous selection has produced a wide range of colours.

Attempts have been made to divide the many species of *Senecio* into a number of genera but they can only be separated on minor and variable characters.

Species with jointed stems and rayless capitula are sometimes put in the genus *Kleinia*. *K. cuneifolia = Senecio cuneatus* [570] is a native of South Africa with thick fleshy leaves and small terminal clusters of cylindrical capitula. *Senecio crassissimus* [571] from Madagascar is another succulent with fleshy leaves which is sometimes grown in greenhouses. Other species are sometimes put in the genus *Ligularia*, for example *L. sibirica = S. sibiricus* [572]. This is a stout perennial from three to four feet high which grows in wet meadows from France to Japan. It has triangular, or kidney-shaped, toothed leaves up to a foot across. The handsome spikes of golden-yellow capitula are produced between July and September. Each capitulum has a few ray florets and a cylindrical group of disc florets.

570
571

The common garden **Marigold** or **Pot-marigold**, *Calendula officinalis* [573], is a native of southern Europe. It is an annual from one to two feet high with oblong, entire, more or less hairy leaves. The orange capitula are produced from June onwards. The fruits are curved and lack a pappus. There is a wide range of forms in cultivation varying in size and flower colour.

Echinops sphaerocephalus [574, 575] is one of the **Globe Thistles** and is a native of south-east Europe and south-west Asia. It is a stout perennial from five to seven feet high with long, pinnatifid spiny leaves covered beneath with white hairs. The spherical flowering heads, each composed of a large number of single-flowered capitula appear in branched terminal clusters during the summer. The florets are pale bluish-grey; the fruit has a pappus of short scales.

573

574

575

Xeranthemum annuum [576], a native of southern Europe, is an annual from one to two feet high with lanceolate, entire leaves. The purple capitula are over an inch across and are produced in July. The inner involucral bracts are spreading and petal-like. The dried capitula persist for many years and in cultivation show a wide range of colours.

Carlina acanthifolia [577] is a biennial thistle from southern Europe. It has spiny pinnatifid leaves and a large yellowish purple capitulum about four inches across.

576

577

578

Carlina acaulis [578] is a European thistle which is
usually found on sunny stony slopes. It has a rosette
of spiny leaves and the large, short-stalked capitulum
is produced in July or August. The involucre consists
of a number of silvery-white radiating bracts which
curl over the central florets during wet weather.
The **Woolly Thistle**, *Cirsium eriophorum* [579, 581],
occurs on calcareous grassland in Britain and

579

Europe. It is a biennial with a grooved stem from two to five feet high and wavy, pinnatifid, spiny leaves. The globular capitula, up to two inches across, are produced between July and September. The involucre consists of numerous spiny bracts thickly covered with cottony hairs. The long tubular florets are reddish-purple and the one-seeded fruits bear very long, shiny, white pappus hairs.

580

581

Cirsium canum [582] is a thistle which grows in moist meadows in central and southern Europe. It reaches three feet in height and has narrow, spiny leaves and red capitula.

The **Lesser Burdock**, *Arctium minus* [580], occurs throughout the British Isles, Europe, North Africa, the Caucasus and North America. It is an extremely variable biennial with a stout tap-root and large basal leaves having hollow stalks and oblong-ovate blades. It reaches a height of from two to four feet. The loosely branched groups of spherical capitula are produced between July and September. The numerous involucral bracts have stiff, hooked tips. All the reddish-purple florets are tubular, and the compressed fruits are crowned with a pappus of short hairs.

Although called the **Scotch Thistle**, *Onopordum acanthium* [583] is in fact rare in Scotland. It has a scattered distribution in England, and occurs in Europe and western Asia as a native and in North America as an introduction. It is a large biennial up to five feet high with a spiny, winged stem covered with woolly hairs. The toothed, elliptical leaves are also spiny. The spherical capitula, which appear between July and September, are about two inches across and surrounded by many spiky bracts. The tubular florets are pale purple and the wrinkled fruits bear reddish pappus hairs.

The **Creeping** or **Canada Thistle**, *Cirsium arvense* [584], a common plant of waste and cultivated land in the British Isles, Europe and Asia, has also been introduced into North America. It is a perennial with long white roots which give rise to the annual erect stems from one to three feet high. The spirally arranged leaves have wavy, spiny margins. The plants are unisexual and the rose-purple capitula appear from July to September. The male capitula are globose with conspicuous anthers, and the female capitula are ovoid with projecting stigmas. The fruits have a radiating tuft of feathery white hairs.

582

583

584

585

The **Spear** or **Bull Thistle**, *Cirsium vulgare* [585], is common in the British Isles, Europe, and western Asia, and it also occurs in many parts of North America. It is a prickly biennial from one to five feet high. The ovoid capitula with pale purple florets appear from July to October.

XIXa   *Punica granatum* (**Pomegranate**, flowers and young fruit)

XIXb   *Punica granatum* (**Pomegranate**, ripe fruit)

XXa *Coffea arabica*

XXb *Aster alpinus*

586

The true **Artichoke**, *Cynara scolymus* [586], is a native of southern Europe and has been widely cultivated for the sake of its large globular capitula.

The numerous fleshy involucral bracts are eaten with the tip of the stem, when young, before the florets are exposed.

587
587
589

588

The **Milk Thistle**, *Silybum marianum* [587], is a
native of southern Europe and the Near East which
has become introduced into Britain, Australia and
North and South America. It is an annual or biennial
from one to four feet high with mottled, spiny leaves.
The ovoid capitula which appear between June and
August have involucral bracts with spreading
yellowish spines and reddish-purple tubular florets.
Saussurea alpina [588] occurs on mountains in
Britain, Europe and Siberia; a related species grows
in North America. It is a perennial with lanceolate
basal leaves. The erect stem, from three to 18 inches
high, bears a terminal cluster of small capitula with
purple florets in August and September.

The **Cornflower** or **Bachelor's Button**, *Centaurea
cyanus* [589], is probably a native of Europe and the
Near East but it has been widely distributed as a

590

591

592

cornfield weed. It is an annual with tough erect stems from one to three feet high. The capitula appear between June and August and are about an inch across. The large marginal tubular florets are bright blue and sterile. The central, smaller tubular florets are reddish-purple and bisexual.

There are about 400 species in the genus *Centaurea*, most being natives of southern Europe and the Near East. *C. orbelica* [590] is a yellow-flowered species which is confined to Bulgaria. *C. montana* [591] occurs commonly in meadows and pastures on European mountains. It is a variable, softly hairy perennial up to three feet high with broadly lanceolate leaves. The large capitula appear between May and July and have bluish-violet marginal neuter florets and reddish-violet bisexual central florets. The fruit has a pappus of rough hairs. *C. pseudophrygia* [592], which occurs in meadows of central Europe, has red capitula.

593

594

Gerbera jamesonii [593, 595], the **Barberton** or **Transvaal Daisy**, is a native of the Transvaal and Natal. It is a hairy perennial with a woody base and numerous lanceolate, pinnatifid leaves from six to 10 inches long. The large, orange-coloured capitula, from three to four inches across, are borne on the ends of long, erect, unbranched stems during the spring and summer. There is a single row of about 30 marginal florets with curved, strap-shaped corollas. The numerous disc florets are somewhat two-lipped. The fruits are beaked and have a pappus of rough hairs. There are a number of forms of this attractive plant in cultivation which vary in colour from white to reddish-orange.

The **Cocklebur**, *Xanthium strumarium* [594], is an American plant which has become a weed of cultivation in many parts of the world and is occasionally found in Britain. It is a greyish-green annual from eight to 30 inches high with long-stalked, triangular, coarsely toothed leaves. The ovoid male capitula are borne near the top of the plant, the ovoid female capitula lower down and enclosed in fused spiny bracts. Each has only two florets and the two flattened one-seeded fruits remain enclosed by the hardened involucre. The hooked spines of the involucre get caught in the fur of animals and thus assist dispersal which is, however, largely by water.

Scolymus hispanicus [596] is a native of the Mediterranean region occasionally cultivated for its edible tap-root. It is a biennial or perennial with erect stems from one to three feet high and oblong-lanceolate spiny leaves. The capitulum consists of a few ray florets and is subtended by three spiny bracts.

Chicory, *Cichorium intybus* [597], is a native of England and Wales, Europe and western Asia but it has become naturalized in most temperate regions including the United States. It is a perennial with a long, thick tap-root and a basal rosette of large lobed leaves. The erect, grooved stems, up to four feet high, are somewhat hairy and bear a few simple narrow leaves. The axillary capitula are produced on the upper stems between June and October. Each is composed of numerous bright blue ray-like ligulate florets surrounded by two rows of green bracts. The capitula

599

600

are open only during the morning hours, when they are pollinated usually by bees. A coffee substitute is made from the dried roots, and the young blanched shoots of a variety are used in salads.

The **Mouse-ear Hawkweed,** *Hieracium pilosella* [598], occurs throughout the British Isles and much of Europe, western Asia and North America on rocks and walls and in dry grassy places. It is a small perennial with a rosette of lanceolate leaves which are covered beneath with a layer of white woolly hairs. It can spread vegetatively by the production of long creeping stolons which give rise to new plantlets. The solitary capitula are about an inch across and appear

between May and August on unbranched stems from two to 12 inches long which arise from the centre of the leaf rosette. All the florets are of one kind with lemon-yellow, strap-shaped, ligulate corollas.

Hypochoeris uniflora [599] is common in high pastures in the Alps, the Sudeten mountains and the Carpathians. It is a perennial with a basal rosette of oblong, toothed, hairy leaves. The solitary capitulum, appearing between July and September, terminates an erect, grooved stem which tapers from the top downwards. It is about two inches across, with several rows of blackish involucral bracts and many bright yellow ligulate florets.

602

The **Rough Hawkbit**, *Leontodon hispidus* [600], occurs on grassland throughout Britain, Europe and Asia Minor. It is a variable perennial with a large rosette of hairy leaves having wavy margins. The solitary capitula are borne on hairy erect stems up to 24 inches long between June and September. The capitulum is from one to two inches across and consists of numerous deep yellow ligulate florets.

Goat's Beard, *Tragopogon pratensis* [601, 602], is a variable perennial which grows in pastures and waste places in the British Isles, Europe, western Asia and North America. It has a long tap-root and long, narrow, hairless leaves. The capitula are borne on branched stems up to two feet high during June and July. The involucre consists of a few long narrow bracts, and the yellow ligulate florets may not exceed them in length. A large spherical fruiting head is produced [602] after flowering. The narrow cylindrical fruit bears a long beak terminating in a spreading ring of pappus hairs. Five of the hairs are long and simple but the rest are feathery and form a parachute which aids wind dispersal.

The **Lime** family, *Tiliaceae*, includes about 300 species of trees or shrubs which are widely distributed in both tropical and temperate regions. The 30 species of *Tilia* are all deciduous trees confined to north temperate areas. The alternate leaves are heart-shaped with toothed margins and each group of small yellowish flowers has a common stalk which is partially fused to an elongated bract. The globose fruit contains one to three seeds.

The **White Lime**, *Tilia tomentosa* [603], is a native of eastern Europe which is frequently planted in parks elsewhere.

The **Large-leaved Lime**, *Tilia platyphyllos* [604], occurs in central and eastern Europe and in Asia as far east as the Caucasus. It is apparently native in a few parts of Britain but has been widely planted. It reaches a height of 100 feet and has leaves up to five inches long which are hairy underneath. There are few flowers in each cluster and the fruits are ribbed.

The **Common Lime** or **Linden**, *T. × europaea*, which is so frequently planted along roadsides and in parks in Europe is a fertile hybrid between *T. platyphyllos* and the **Small-leaved Lime,** *T. cordata*. It reaches a height of 90 feet and shows variable characters intermediate between those of its parents. Its leaves are always infected by aphids which produce a large amount of sticky honey-dew. **Basswood**, *T. americana*, is a common tree of North America, often planted.

603

604

The 750 species belonging to the family *Sterculiaceae* are mainly tropical trees and shrubs. *Dombeya wallichii* [605] from Madagascar is a tree up to 30 feet high with velvety, heart-shaped leaves and dense pendulous clusters of scarlet flowers. The **Cacao Tree**, *Theobroma cacao* [606, 607], is a small tree from tropical America which is now widely cultivated in warm areas for the cocoa prepared from the fermented seeds. It has alternate lanceolate leaves and the small flowers [607] are produced directly on the older branches. The fleshy fruit is about eight inches long and contains 30 to 60 seeds.

The family *Bombacaceae* includes about 140 species of tropical trees most of which are American. However, the **Baobab**, *Adansonia digitata* [608], is a native of west and central Africa. It attains a height of 60 feet and has an extremely thick trunk. It has compound palmate leaves and the solitary flowers are up to six inches across. The fruit is edible and a strong fibre is produced from the bark. The **Silk-cotton Tree**, *Ceiba pentandra* [609], is a large tree up to 100 feet high with spreading basal flanges. Kapok is obtained from the hairy seeds.

605

606

607

609

610

The **Mallow** family, *Malvaceae* [610–618], includes at least 1,000 species which are world-wide in distribution but are particularly common in the tropical regions of America. They may be trees, shrubs or herbs with mucilaginous sap and spirally arranged leaves which are frequently palmately lobed. The flowers are often large and showy with a funnel- or saucer-shaped corolla composed of five free petals. The filaments of the numerous stamens are joined at the base forming a tube surrounding the central style. The fruit is either a capsule or breaks up into one-seeded portions. The family is of great economic importance for the production of cotton, and various species are grown for ornamental purposes.

There are many forms of **Cotton**, *Gossypium* spp. [610, 611], but botanists vary in their opinion about the actual number of species. They are stout herbs or shrubs with alternate, lobed leaves. The flower [610], which may be purple, yellow or white, has five large bracts surrounding the entire calyx and a funnel-shaped corolla.

The fruit is a capsule which on drying opens to expose the long hairs of the numerous small seeds [611]. The commercial cottons can be divided into two main groups. The New World group includes the Sea Island and Egyptian cottons, *G. barbadense*, the American Upland cotton, *G. hirsutum*, and the tropical tree cottons from South America such as *G. brasiliense*. The Old World group includes the Levant Cotton, *G. herbaceum*, and the Indian cotton, *G. neglectum*. *Kitaibelia vitifolia* [612] is a native of Bosnia and Serbia. It is a stout perennial herb with large, lobed, toothed leaves and attractive white flowers.

611

612

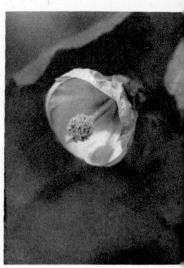

613
615

The genus *Pavonia* includes about 100 species of widespread tropical herbs. *P. multiflora* [613], various cultivated forms of which are known as *P. intermedia*, is a stout, often unbranched plant from Brazil. The leaves are broadly lanceolate and each flower has a circle of narrow reddish bracts around the reduced calyx. The column of stamens projects well beyond the edge of the erect petals.

There are about 80 species of *Abutilon* which may be herbs, shrubs or trees widely scattered in warmer parts of the earth. The flower [614] is bell-shaped and often yellow. The plants frequently grown in cool greenhouses are varieties and hybrids of several herbaceous species. Particularly common are hybrids between the Brazilian species *A. striatum* and *A. darwinii* included under the horticultural name *A. hybridum*.

The **Chinese Hibiscus**, *Hibiscus rosa-sinensis* [615], is a shrub which attains a height of from three to eight feet when grown in greenhouses but reaches 30 feet under subtropical conditions. It has shiny, ovate, toothed leaves and solitary, rose-red flowers from four to five inches across. *H. syriacus* [coloured plate XIV] is a deciduous shrub about six feet high with large bell-shaped flowers. It is a variable species and there are numerous named varieties in cultivation.

The **Marsh Mallow**, *Althaea officinalis* [616], occurs in marshes, usually near the sea, in the British Isles, Europe, western Asia and North Africa. It is an erect hairy perennial up to four feet high with coarsely toothed leaves. The pale pink axillary flowers are nearly two inches across and appear in August and September. The abundant mucilage present in the roots was used for making sweets, but has been largely replaced by synthetic materials.

The **Hollyhock**, *Althaea rosea* [617], is a native of China. It is a tall perennial herb which is usually treated as a biennial in gardens. The rounded leaf blades can be up to a foot across. The flowers, of various colours and up to three inches across, are borne in axillary clusters.

Lavatera thuringiaca [618] is a hairy perennial herb from Armenia and the Caucasus with three- to five-lobed leaves and pink flowers.

616
617

The **Spurge** family, *Euphorbiaceae* [619–636, coloured plate XV], includes at least 7,000 widely spread species. They vary greatly in habit and may be trees, shrubs, herbs or succulents and always have a milky sap. The simple or compound leaves are alternate. The small flowers are unisexual and the perianth is reduced or absent. The ovary usually has three cells and the fruit is a capsule. The family is of considerable economic importance. Many are also grown as ornamentals, including **Poinsettias**, e.g. *Euphorbia pulcherrima* [coloured plate XV].
The **Red-hot Cat-tail** or **Chenille Plant**, *Acalypha hispida* [619], is a native of Burma and the East Indies. It is an erect perennial which is frequently cultivated for its long pendulous spikes of small red flowers.
The **Castor-oil Plant**, *Ricinus communis* [620, 621, 623], is believed to be a native of Africa but it is now widely grown and has become naturalized in various tropical and temperate areas. In the tropics it can attain the proportions of a small tree 40 feet in height. The large alternate leaves have long stalks and palmately lobed blades. The small crowded male flowers have many stamens with branched filaments. The ovaries of the female flowers are covered with persistent spines.

621

622

The fruit [623] is an ovoid capsule which splits vertically to release and eject three large seeds. Each seed [621] has a smooth, hard, attractively mottled coat and a large white body, the caruncle, attached at the base. The seeds are poisonous but the extracted oil is rendered harmless by heating. There are many forms of this plant but all referable to the one species. *Dalechampia roezliana* [622, 624] is a native of Mexico. It is an erect shrub up to four feet high with large, lanceolate, coarsely toothed leaves. The small dense group of yellow unisexual flowers is surrounded by two large pale red bracts.

623

624

Monadenium guentheri [625] is an erect plant from tropical Africa with spreading spatulate leaves. It is closely allied to *Euphorbia* but differs in details of the inflorescence.

The **Cassava** or **Tapioca Plant**, *Manihot utilissima* [626], is a native of Brazil which has been cultivated since early times and widely planted in other tropical regions. It is still the staple food of many South American Indians. It is a stout herbaceous plant up to nine feet high with large palmate leaves. The basal clusters of thick cylindrical roots contain abundant starch. They are also more or less poisonous owing to the presence of hydrocyanic acid, but this is destroyed on heating during the manufacture of tapioca and other foods.

The large and widely distributed genus *Euphorbia* consists of at least 1,600 species. They range in habit from small annual herbs to quite large trees. The basic unit of the inflorescence is a small, fleshy, cup-shaped structure, the cyathium, which contains a central stalked female flower and several male flowers each consisting of a single stamen. Variously shaped and coloured glands occur on the rim of the cyathium which thus resembles a single flower. They are grouped together in compound umbellate inflorescences subtended by large leafy bracts.

625

626

Wolf's-milk or Leafy Spurge, *Euphorbia esula* [627], is widespread in Europe and western Asia and in a few places in Britain where it may be a native. It is a perennial with a creeping rhizome and numerous erect stems bearing narrow leaves. The flowers appear between May and July. **Crown-of-thorns**, *E. splendens* [628], from Madagascar has a thick fleshy stem covered with thorns. The pairs of subtending bracts of the inflorescence are scarlet. **Ghostweed** or **Snow-on-the-Mountains**, *E. marginata* [629], a native of the western areas of the United States, has large inflorescence bracts and the glands on the rim of each cyathium look like small white petals; the leaves have white margins.

627

629

628

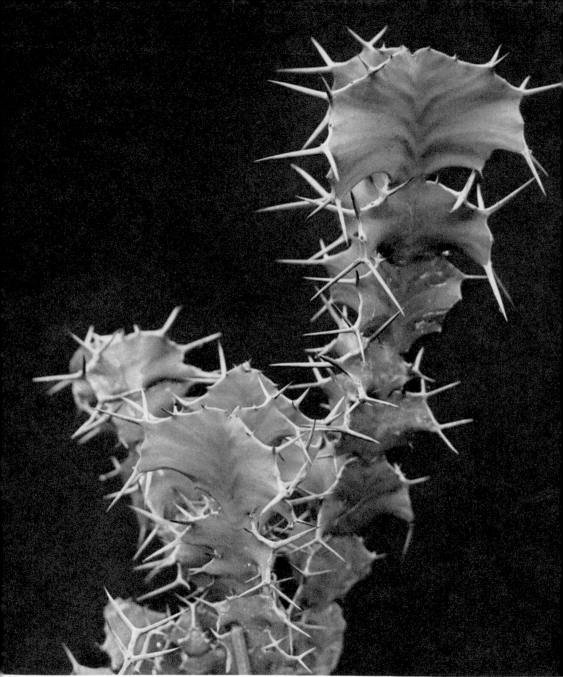

630

A number of species of *Euphorbia* are succulents and closely resemble cacti although they are not related to the *Cactaceae* (p. 146). The latter are limited to the New World whereas *Euphorbia* spp. occur in both hemispheres. In many Old World species the main stem is reduced to a fleshy, flattened or cylindrical column, the leaves to thorns and the lateral branches to tufts of hairs. Two good examples from South

631

Africa are *E. grandicornis* [630] and *E. ledienii* [631]. The latter has a greyish-green, ridged stem up to six feet high which has numerous yellow glandular inflorescences. *E. obesa* [632] is more or less spherical and has no spines. The plants are unisexual, the one illustrated being female. *E. pulvinata* [633] has a thick, ridged, columnar trunk and rows of purplish thorns which represent aborted inflorescence stalks.

632

E. *bupleurifolia* [634] has a thick trunk about four inches high covered with small spherical tufts of hairs. A few narrow leaves are produced at the top during the summer. E. *meloformis* [635] has a spherical, deeply ridged stem. The ribs bear scars of the fallen inflorescences. There are numerous cultivated hybrids and varieties including monstrous forms resulting from the multiple crossing of E.

634

633

635

636

obesa × *meloformis* × *globosa* [636]. The numerous American species are mostly herbaceous weeds, such as *E. corollata*, *E. maculata*, and **Painted-leaf** or **Fire-on-the-Mountain**, *E. heterophylla*.

321

The tropical American family *Erythroxylaceae* includes over 200 species most of which belong to the genus *Erythroxylon*. They are all shrubs or trees with simple opposite leaves and small bisexual flowers. There are usually 10 stamens more or less fused basally. The fruit is usually succulent.

The most important member economically is the **Coca**, *Erythroxylon coca* [637], which is a native of the Andes of Peru and Bolivia. It is a shrub from 10 to 15 feet high. The important drug cocaine which is used as a local anaesthetic is obtained from its leaves and it is now widely cultivated in tropical countries.

637

638

Most of the 900 species of the **Oxalis** family, *Oxalidaceae* [638–641], are herbs found in both tropical and temperate areas. They often have fleshy rhizomes or tubers and the alternate leaves are compound. The bisexual flowers have five sepals, five petals, 10 stamens fused basally and a central ovary with five styles. Frequently the fruit is a capsule and the elastic seed coat forcibly ejects the seed.

The **Wood Sorrel**, *Oxalis acetosella* [638], is widespread in the British Isles, Europe and Asia. It is often found in the dense shade of woods and among rocks. It is a small perennial with a thin creeping rhizome and alternate, trifoliolate leaves. The solitary flowers, which appear mostly

639

640

323

641

642

in April and May, have white petals with mauve veins. Most of the capsules with viable seeds are produced in summer from flowers which never open and are self-pollinated.

O. ortgiesii [639] comes from Peru, *O. adenophylla* [640] from Chile, and *O. bupleurifolia* [641] from Brazil. The last has flattened leaf stalks and reduced blades. Several species are common weeds in lawns and waste places.

The family *Linaceae* includes nearly 300 species of temperate and tropical herbs, shrubs and trees, of which at least 200 belong to the **Flax** genus, *Linum*. The cultivated **Flax**, *L. usitatissimum*, from which linen fibres and linseed oil are obtained, is of unknown origin. *L. austriacum* [643] is an erect plant from one to two feet high with pale blue flowers which grows in the Austrian Alps. A number of species with yellow flowers are native in the United States.

643

644

645

There are at least 700 species in the **Geranium** family, *Geraniaceae* [642, 644–648]. They are mostly herbs widely distributed in temperate and subtropical regions. The leaves are lobed or compound and arranged alternately on the stem. The bisexual flower has five sepals, five petals and five or 10 stamens. The ovary is three- to five-celled and gives rise to a lobed capsule.

The **Meadow Cranesbill**, *Geranium pratense* [642, 644],

is widespread in Britain, Europe and north and central Asia. It has become naturalized in North America. It is a perennial herb with a thick rhizome and erect stems up to three feet high. The basal leaves have long stalks and palmately lobed blades with pinnately dissected lobes. The stem leaves are simpler and smaller. The large violet-blue cup-shaped flowers appear in axillary pairs between June and September. The basal region of the fruit,

646

325

647

648

surrounded by the persistent calyx, has five lobes each containing a single seed. On drying the thickened style splits into five longitudinal strips attached to the top of a central column. When a strip coils upwards suddenly it carries a lobe of the capsule with it and the seed is thrown out. The American **Wild Geranium**, *G. maculatum*, is similar.

The **Bloody** or **Blood-red Cranesbill**, *Geranium sanguineum* [646], is a small perennial found in woods and grassy places throughout the British Isles, Europe and western Asia and often cultivated. The leaf blades are rounded with narrow, pointed blades. The crimson-purple flowers are produced in July and August.

The **Common Storksbill** or **Alfileria**, *Erodium cicutarium* [645], is a widespread variable annual in dry sandy places throughout the British Isles, Europe, Asia and North Africa. It has become naturalized in both North and South America. The leaves are more or less pinnately divided. Between one and nine small pinkish-purple flowers are borne in each long-stalked axillary cluster between June and September. The fruit is similar to that of the **Cranesbill** but each stylar strip becomes detached with the one-seeded lobe. *E. chamaedryoides* [647] is a small species with white pink-veined flowers from Corsica and the Balearic Islands.

The well-known **Garden Geraniums** are selected varieties and hybrids of numerous species of *Pelargonium* [648]. *P. cucullatum* from South Africa is a parent of many garden forms.

The **Nasturtium** family, *Tropaeolaceae*, includes about 50 species of the genus *Tropaeolum* which is distributed mainly in the mountains from Mexico to Chile and Argentina. The species most frequently cultivated is *T. majus* [649, coloured plate XVIb] from Peru. There are numerous varieties and also hybrids between this and other species. It is an annual climber with weak stems and alternate, peltate leaves. The large bisexual flower has five sepals, one being spurred. In the wild plant there are five orange petals but in cultivation double and semidouble flowers of various colours are known. The fruit consists of three one-seeded portions.

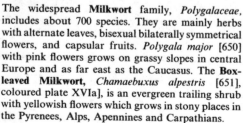

651

652

The widespread **Milkwort** family, *Polygalaceae,* includes about 700 species. They are mainly herbs with alternate leaves, bisexual bilaterally symmetrical flowers, and capsular fruits. *Polygala major* [650] with pink flowers grows on grassy slopes in central Europe and as far east as the Caucasus. The **Box-leaved Milkwort,** *Chamaebuxus alpestris* [651], coloured plate XVIa], is an evergreen trailing shrub with yellowish flowers which grows in stony places in the Pyrenees, Alps, Apennines and Carpathians.

The **Rue** family, *Rutaceae* [652-659], is a large family of some 1,300 species which are widely distributed in the temperate regions of both the northern and southern hemispheres. They have a wide range of habit; all are characterized by the presence of translucent dots on the leaves, the lobed ovary raised on a central disc and the presence of glands that secrete aromatic oils. The family is of economic importance for the citrus fruits, orange, lemon, grapefruit, lime and tangerine, and also for various ornamental plants.

653

654

The **Burning Bush**, *Dictamnus albus* [652], is a perennial up to two feet high with compound glossy leaves. The terminal spikes of white, pink or purplish flowers are produced in June and July. This plant is a native of eastern Europe and Asia and is easily grown in ordinary garden soil. It secretes so much volatile oil that on a warm windless day it can burst into flame at the touch of a match.

The **Mexican Orange Blossom**, *Choisia ternata* [653], is an evergreen shrub up to 10 feet high. It has opposite

655

656

657

658

trifoliolate leaves with entire lanceolate leaflets. The terminal clusters of scented white flowers appear between June and November.

The **Japanese Skimmia**, *Skimmia japonica* [654], is an evergreen shrub about four feet high with alternate leathery ovate leaves which are bright green above and much paler below. The small yellowish-white flowers appear in dense clusters during April. They are unisexual and the male and female flowers appear on different plants. The fruit is a bright red berry.

The **Hop Tree**, *Ptelea trifoliata* [655, 656], is a native of North America which is frequently grown in parks in other temperate regions. It reaches a height of 15 feet and has alternate trifoliolate leaves with finely toothed, ovate leaflets. The terminal clusters of small greenish-white flowers are produced in June. The circular winged fruits [656] are about an inch across and are very like those of the Elm. The genus *Citrus* includes a few native species of eastern Asia but they have been cultivated for so long in the warm parts of the world for their valuable fruits that their delimitation is difficult. They are small evergreen trees with leathery leaves which are jointed between the winged leaf-stalk and blade. The fragrant flowers are white and the large fruit is a berry.

330

The true **Mandarin Orange** is *C. nobilis* [657]. The true **Oranges** are considered to be varieties of *C. aurantium* such as the **Seville Orange**, var. *amara*, the **Bergamotte**, var. *bergama*, and the **Sweet Orange**, var. *sinensis*, although some authorities consider these to be separate species. *C. medica* is considered to be the parent of the **Citron**, the **Lime**, var. *acida*, and the **Lemon**, var. *limonum* [658]. The **Grapefruit** is *C. paradisi*.

Poncirus trifoliata [659] is a native of northern China and Korea. It is a thorny shrub with trifoliolate leaves and small, hairy, inedible fruits.

The family *Simaroubaceae* includes about 200 species of trees and shrubs most of which are tropical. They all have alternate, pinnately compound leaves and usually the flowers are unisexual with the flowers on separate trees.

The **Tree of Heaven**, *Ailanthus altissima* [660], is a native of China but is often planted in towns of temperate regions because it is quick-growing and can tolerate a polluted atmosphere. It is a deciduous tree up to 70 feet in height with a smooth bark and large pinnate leaves. The small greenish flowers are borne in pendulous groups (the male flowers emit a disagreeable odour) and the elongated, flattened fruit contains a single seed.

659

660

661

662

The *Celastraceae* is a cosmopolitan family of about 500 species of woody climbers, shrubs or trees. The leaves are simple, alternate or opposite and the small greenish flowers are usually bisexual. The fruits are of various types but the seed is often surrounded by a fleshy layer, the aril. The family is of little economic importance but a number of species are grown for ornament.

The 120 species of the genus *Euonymus* are widespread in Europe, Asia and northern and central America. The **Spindle Tree**, *E. europaeus* [661, 662], occurs in Europe and western Asia and is found throughout most of the British Isles, usually in woods on alkaline soils. It is a deciduous tree or shrub up to 20 feet high with a smooth grey bark and opposite, ovate, pointed leaves. The flowers appear in May or June in small stiff axillary groups. They may be bisexual or unisexual and have widely separated, greenish petals. The rounded fruit [662] is a distinctly four-lobed fleshy capsule which is deep pink when mature. On splitting open, the bright orange fleshy arils of the few seeds are exposed. The fruits and seeds together with the tinted foliage make the tree very attractive in the autumn. The wood is hard and was formerly used for making skewers and spindles. **Wahoo**, *E. atropurpureus*, and **Strawberry-bush**, *E. americanus*, are common species of North America.

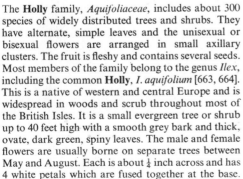

663

664

The **Holly** family, *Aquifoliaceae*, includes about 300 species of widely distributed trees and shrubs. They have alternate, simple leaves and the unisexual or bisexual flowers are arranged in small axillary clusters. The fruit is fleshy and contains several seeds. Most members of the family belong to the genus *Ilex*, including the common **Holly**, *I. aquifolium* [663, 664]. This is a native of western and central Europe and is widespread in woods and scrub throughout most of the British Isles. It is a small evergreen tree or shrub up to 40 feet high with a smooth grey bark and thick, ovate, dark green, spiny leaves. The male and female flowers are usually borne on separate trees between May and August. Each is about ¼ inch across and has 4 white petals which are fused together at the base.

The spherical scarlet berries are found on the female plants between September and March.

The **Holly** is used as Christmas decoration; and as it can withstand clipping it forms an excellent, compact, slow-growing hedge. A number of varieties are commonly grown in parks and gardens including those with variegated foliage or yellow berries.

Several other species are sometimes cultivated including *I. opaca* from the eastern United States which is very similar to the common **Holly** but has conspicuous veins on the lower surfaces of the leaves. A number of deciduous species also grow in the United States; **Inkberry**, *I. glabra*, **Black-alder** or **Winterberry**, *I. verticillata*, and **Possum-haw**, *I. decidua*, are among the most widespread.

333

665

The small **Bladdernut** family, *Staphyleaceae*, includes
some 24 species of trees and shrubs found mostly in
north temperate regions.

Staphylea pinnata [665], a deciduous species of
southern Europe, reaches a height of 15 feet. It has
opposite pinnate leaves with ovate toothed leaflets.
The drooping clusters of pinkish-white flowers appear
in May. The fruit is an inflated capsule. The **American
Bladdernut**, *S. trifolia*, is found from Quebec to
Georgia and westwards to Minnesota and Oklahoma.

666

The **Olive** family, *Oleaceae* [666-676, coloured plate XVII], includes about 500 species widely distributed, and particularly common in Asia and the East Indies. They are trees or shrubs which usually have opposite leaves. The flowers are mostly bisexual and have four- or six-lobed corollas, two stamens and a two-celled ovary. The fruit is a capsule, fleshy or winged and indehiscent. The family is of economic importance for the oil and wood obtained from the Olive, the timber of various species of Ash and a number of attractive ornamental shrubs.

Forsythia suspensa [666] is a deciduous shrub up to 10 feet high with arching branches and simple opposite, toothed leaves about four inches long. The shortly stalked yellow flowers are about an inch long and appear in early spring before the leaves unfold. The fruit is a capsule. This species is a native of China, frequently cultivated. Other species which are commonly grown in gardens include *F. viridissima* with stiff, erect, green branches and long lanceolate leaves and the early flowering *F. ovata* with small ovate leaves.

One of the most popular commonly grown species of *Jasminum*, is *J. nudiflorum* [coloured plate XVII], the **Winter Jasmine**. It is a deciduous rambling plant from China and Japan with slender, angled stems and shortly stalked, trifoliate leaves. The solitary, axillary flowers appear between November and February. Each has a yellow tubular corolla with six spreading lobes. The fruit is a black berry.

667
668

The genus *Syringa* includes about 30 species, most of which are cultivated. The **Common Lilac**, *S. vulgaris* [667], is a native of south-eastern Europe. It is a small tree or shrub up to 20 feet high which produces suckers freely at the base. The thin, opposite leaves are ovate. The dense pyramidal inflorescences of small, tubular, fragrant flowers are produced in May. There are many varieties in cultivation with flowers from white to deep purple in colour. The fruit is an oblong capsule.

669

S. *reflexa* [668] is a smaller shrub from China. It has
lanceolate to ovate leaves and in June it produces long,
narrow clusters of deep pink flowers. The **Rouen Lilac**,

S. *chinensis* [669], is a hybrid with small, lanceolate
leaves. The large drooping masses of white or purplish
flowers appear in May.

670

The **Common Privet**, *Ligustrum vulgare* [670, 671], is frequently found on calcareous soils in England and Wales, most of Europe and North Africa. It is a more or less deciduous shrub up to 15 feet high with smooth, lanceolate leaves about two inches long. The loose clusters of small white flowers [670] appear in June and July. The fruit [671] is a shiny, spherical black berry which contains from two to four seeds. Although at one time often planted for hedges this species has now been largely replaced by *L. ovalifolium* from Japan and its variety var. *variegatum*, the **Golden Privet.**

672

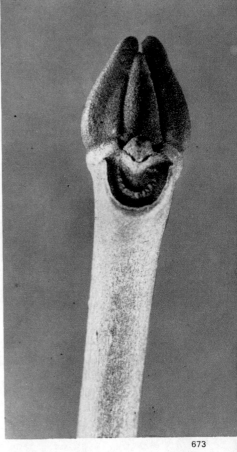

673

674

The **Common Ash**, *Fraxinus excelsior* [672–674], is widely distributed in Britain where it forms woods on calcareous soils particularly in wetter parts of the country. It is also found throughout most of Europe, western Asia and North Africa. It is a deciduous tree sometimes reaching 120 feet in height. The rough bark is pale grey and the characteristic buds [673] are covered with hard black scales. The opposite, pinnate leaves are up to a foot long and have between seven and 13 lanceolate, toothed leaflets. The dense clusters of small purplish flowers are borne on the sides of the twigs in April and May before the leaves unfold [672]. Some of the flowers are bisexual, others unisexual and none of them has a perianth. The familiar brown, twisted, one-seeded fruits or 'keys' hang in conspicuous bunches [674]. Common American species are **Red Ash**, *F. pennsylvania*, **White Ash**, *F. americana*, **Blue Ash**, *F. quadrangulata*, and **Pop-ash**, *F. caroliniana*.

676

The **Olive**, *Olea europaea* [675, 676], is a native of the
Mediterranean region where it has been extensively
cultivated since ancient times. It is now grown also in
California. It is an evergreen tree up to 40 feet high
with a spreading crown and grey bark. Young trees
have a single erect trunk but frequently this splits and
old trees have several contorted trunks [676]. The
opposite, simple leaves are about three inches long
with short stalks and leathery, lanceolate or ovate
blades which are pale below and dull green above.
The small, white, insignificant flowers are borne in
axillary groups. The ripe ovoid purplish-black
fruits, which can be found on the trees throughout the
year, each contain a single hard stone.

The **Olive** is of great economic importance. The green
unripe fruits are pickled in salt or vinegar and eaten
as a savoury. Olive oil is obtained by pressing the ripe
fruit. The best edible oil, the almost colourless virgin
oil is obtained by lightly pressing the fruit in the cold.
A second, rather stronger pressing produces a clear
yellow edible oil. The so-called tree oil, which is used
as a fuel and in the manufacture of soap, is obtained
from a third pressing under heat. The wood is used in
cabinet-making and turnery.

677

678

The family *Menyanthaceae* is closely related to the *Gentianaceae* (p. 344) but all its members are aquatic or bog plants with alternate, not opposite leaves. It includes about 35 species which have a cosmopolitan distribution.

The genus *Menyanthes* is confined to a single species *M. trifoliata* [677, 678], the **Bogbean**. It is found at the edges of lakes and ponds and in the wet parts of fens and bogs. It is widely distributed in the British Isles, Europe, northern and central Asia, North America, Greenland and Iceland. It is a perennial with a creeping rhizome and large trifoliolate leaves which are raised above the surface of the water. The erect leafless stems are up to a foot long and bear a terminal cluster of from 10 to 20 beautiful white flowers between May and July. Each flower is over half an inch across and the inner surfaces of the five narrow corolla lobes are covered with numerous white filaments. The flowers may have long or short styles, the two kinds being found on different plants. The fruit is a rounded capsule which opens by two valves to release the numerous small seeds.

679

There are about 20 species of *Nymphoides*, most of which are tropical or subtropical. They are aquatic plants and have rounded, floating leaves resembling those of the water-lilies. One species, the so-called **Fringed Water-lily** or **Yellow Floating-heart**, *N. peltata* [679], grows in ponds and slow-flowing rivers in central and southern Europe, northern and western Asia, the Himalayas and Japan. It is also native in central and eastern England and has become naturalized in North America. It has a creeping rhizome and the alternate leaves have long stalks and floating blades up to four inches across. The long, flowering stems have opposite leaves and the flowers themselves

are borne in small axillary groups during July and August. The corolla is over an inch across and has five yellow fringed lobes. Like those of the **Bogbean** the styles may be short or long. The ovoid beaked fruit is a capsule which becomes detached before it is ripe. It eventually breaks open irregularly and the seeds, which are covered with hairs enabling them to float, are carried away by water currents. A North American species, **Floating-heart**, *N. cordatum*, is found in ponds from Newfoundland to Ontario, Florida and Louisiana. The leaves have heart-shaped blades about two inches long and the flowers are very small.

680

The **Gentian** family, *Gentianaceae* [680–687], includes about 800 species of herbaceous plants which are mainly temperate in distribution. A number are alpine plants. The simple, opposite leaves usually have no stalks. The flowers are bisexual and the more or less funnel-shaped corolla bears five stamens on its inner surface. The fruit, which is a capsule containing many small seeds, is surrounded by the persistent corolla. The family is of little economic importance apart from the numerous species cultivated in gardens.

Gentiana clusii [680] occurs on calcareous and dolomitic rocks at high elevations in the central and eastern Alps and Carpathians. It is a small perennial

XXI *Lilium tigrinum* (**Tiger Lily**)

XXII *Haemanthus hybridus*

681

up to four inches high with lanceolate leathery leaves and beautiful dark blue flowers which appear between April and August. *G. angustifolia* [681] is confined to calcareous rocks of the western Alps and Jura mountains. It is a stoloniferous perennial from

two to four inches high with narrow glistening leaves. The erect flowers have bright blue funnel-shaped corollas about two inches long.

The **Spring Gentian**, *G. verna* [682], is widespread on the mountains of central and southern Europe and

682

northern and central Asia. It is also found in a few localities of the British Isles in limestone grassland. It is a perennial about two inches high with underground stems and persistent rosettes of ovate leaves. The solitary terminal flowers, which appear between April and June, are about an inch long and have intense dark blue corollas with spreading lobes.

G. asclepiadea [683] occurs up to subalpine elevations in mountains of southern and central Europe. It is a perennial from one to two feet high with pale green lanceolate

684

685

leaves. The flowers have narrow, dark blue, purple-spotted corollas and appear in groups from July to September. *G. punctata* [684] is found at alpine elevations in the Alps and Carpathians. It is a perennial with stiff erect stems up to two feet high and elliptical leaves. The flowers are borne in whorls between July and September. Each has a pale yellow purple-spotted corolla about 1½ inches long. *G. lutea* [685] occurs on the mountains of Europe and Asia Minor. It is a perennial from four to six feet high with ovate leaves and whorls of pale yellow flowers which appear in July and August. This is the medicinal Gentian-root. Many other fine gentians occur in the United States, principally in the mountains; though the **Fringed Gentian**, *G. crinita*, is a well-known lowland species. *Swertia perennis* [686] is an alpine bog plant widespread in the mountains of Europe and Asia. It also occurs in Colorado and from Utah northwards. It is a perennial up to a foot high with steel-blue flowers.

The **Common Centaury**, *Centaurium erythraea* [687], is widespread in Britain, Europe and western Asia and has become naturalized in North America. It is an annual, from one to 20 inches high, with elliptical leaves and dense clusters of pink flowers produced between July and October.

686

687

688

689

The family *Apocynaceae* [688–689] includes over 1,000 species most of which are tropical or subtropical plants. They are generally woody with a milky sap and opposite simple leaves. The bisexual flowers have tubular corollas and the anthers of the five epipetalous stamens form a ring around the head of the central style. The fruits are of various kinds. The main economic importance of the family is for the many ornamental plants it provides including **Oleander** (*Nerium*) and **Periwinkle** (*Vinca*).

The **Winter-sweet**, *Acocanthera spectabilis* [688], is a native of South Africa. It is an evergreen shrub up to 15 feet high with dark green, leathery elliptical leaves. The large clusters of fragrant, pure white flowers are produced early in the year. The fruit is a globose, purplish-black berry containing a single seed. The sap and the fruit are very poisonous.

Cerbera odollam [689] is an evergreen shrub from the tropical regions of Asia. It has entire elliptical leaves and white funnel-shaped flowers. All parts of the plant are poisonous.

690

691

The **Milkweed** family, *Asclepiadaceae* [690–696], probably includes at least 1,800 species. They are mainly tropical, being found especially in South America, but many occur in the temperate regions of both hemispheres. The genus *Asclepias*, the **Milkweeds**, includes many species of North America and Africa. They may be herbs, shrubs or small trees with a milky sap. The leaves are generally simple, entire and borne in opposite pairs or are whorls but in some succulent forms they may be reduced or shed at an early stage. The bisexual flowers have five sepals and a five-lobed corolla often with a ring-like corona at the top of the tube. The five stamens are often more or less fused to the gynoecium and their anthers, which bear apical appendages forming a ring around the stigma. The pollen grains contained in the anther lobes are often stuck together to form club-shaped

pollinia which are joined together in pairs. The fruit is a follicle containing few seeds.

Vincetoxicum officinale [690] is a native of Europe, North Africa and Asia as far eastwards as the Himalayas. It is a perennial with a mass of thick adventitious roots and erect stems from one to four feet high. The leaves are broadly lanceolate. The whitish flowers, which are about ½ inch across, are borne in terminal clusters in July and August. The narrow pointed fruit contains a few seeds each with a thick tuft of silky hairs at one end.

Hoya bella [691] is a slender drooping plant from one to two feet high with ovate, dark green leaves. The flowers are borne in short-stalked pendulous clusters. Each is about ¾ inch long, pure white with a deep red or purple centre. This attractive plant, a native of India, is sometimes grown in greenhouses.

349

692

Most of the 80 to 100 species of **Carrion Plants**, *Stapelia* spp., are natives of South Africa. They are succulent, cactus-like plants with thick, angled, leafless stems covered with tubercles. The large fleshy flowers are frequently mottled with dull colours and produce a foetid odour. *S. variegata* [692]

693

has freely branching erect stems up to six inches high. The flowers are from two to three inches across and have five pointed lobes and a large central disc. The corolla is often pale yellow with purplish-brown patches and bands but the colours are variable and many forms have been described.

S. desmetiana [694] has thick velvety stems about a foot high. The large flowers have reflexed, wrinkled lobes which are pale to dark purple. The margins of the corolla lobes and the centre of the flower bear numerous long white hairs. *Ceropegia radicans* [693] which comes from South Africa, has small, fleshy, ovate leaves. The erect flower has a long slender corolla tube and the five lobes are joined at the top. Insects enter the tube through gaps between the lobes and effect pollination.

Caralluma europaea [695] is a Mediterranean plant with fleshy, four-angled stems. The flowers are pale yellow with purple bands and are clustered at the top of the stem. *Fockea capensis* [696], from the desert regions of South Africa, has a thick root and thin untidy branches with small leaves and grey-green flowers.

695

696

353

697

The family *Proteaceae* includes about 1,200 species, the majority of which are found in the drier regions of South Africa and Australia. They are mostly trees or shrubs with alternate, simple or pinnately dissected leaves. The bisexual flowers are frequently borne in conspicuous clusters. Each flower has four perianth parts, four stamens, and a long style which projects beyond the perianth. *Grevillea sulphurea* [697] is an Australian shrub up to six feet high with narrow leaves and terminal clusters of pale yellow flowers.

The 1,000 species belonging to the **Mistletoe** family, *Loranthaceae*, are mainly tropical shrubs partially parasitic on trees. They have thick, simple green leaves, branched stems and absorptive haustoria which penetrate the host tissues. The flowers are small, sometimes unisexual, and often brightly coloured. The fruit is succulent and contains few seeds.

The **Mistletoe**, *Viscum album* [699], occurs on a wide range of deciduous trees but is particularly common on apples. It is widespread in England, Europe and Asia. It is a slightly woody evergreen with narrow, greenish-yellow leaves. The inconspicuous flowers are borne in small groups, the male and female flowers on different plants. The flowers open between February and April but the spherical, white, sticky berries are not ripe until the following December.

The family *Elaeagnaceae* [698, 700] includes about 40 species of shrubs and trees found mostly in north temperate and subtropical regions. The twigs and under surfaces of the leaves are covered with a thick layer of white or brown hairs. The small flowers are unisexual or bisexual and the fruit is a one-seeded achene surrounded by the persistent fleshy perianth.

The **Oleaster**, *Elaeagnus angustifolia* [698], occurs in southern Europe and western Asia as far as the Himalayas. It is a deciduous shrub or small tree up to 20 feet high with alternate, simple, lanceolate leaves about three inches long. The small, yellow, scented flowers appear in axillary clusters during June. The yellow oval fruits are covered with silvery scales.

698

699

700

701

Sea Buckthorn, *Hippophae rhamnoides* [700], is widespread in Europe and Asia especially on coastal sand or shingle. It is a thorny, branched deciduous shrub from three to 10 feet high with silvery lanceolate leaves. The minute greenish flowers are wind-pollinated; they appear in March or April.

The family *Thymelaeaceae* includes about 500 species of shrubs or trees with alternate simple leaves and bisexual flowers. **Mezereon**, *Daphne mezereum* [701, coloured plate XVIII], is a slightly branched deciduous shrub up to four feet high with narrow leaves, purple flowers and scarlet fleshy fruits. It is distributed throughout Europe and temperate Asia and is a rare plant in chalk woodlands of England. *D. arbuscula* [702] is a dwarf evergreen with pink flowers restricted to a small area of central Europe.

The large tropical **Myrtle** family, *Myrtaceae* [703–708], includes about 3,000 species, many of which are found in tropical America or Australia. They are trees or shrubs with opposite, simple leaves and bisexual flowers which have numerous stamens and one-celled ovaries. The family is of considerable economic importance for various edible fruits, oils and ornamental plants.

The **Brazil-nut**, *Bertholletia excelsa* [703], is a large tree with leathery leaves up to two feet long. The creamy-white flowers have six petals. The rounded, hard-shelled fruit, about six inches across, contains about 20 large edible 'nuts' which are, in fact, seeds.

703

705

706

The **Myrtle**, *Myrtus communis* [704], is common in the Mediterranean region. It is an aromatic evergreen shrub up to 12 feet high with shiny lanceolate leaves. The solitary axillary flowers are white and the fruit is a bluish-black berry.

The Australian **Brush Cherry**, *Eugenia myrtifolia* [705], is a tree up to 80 feet high, with lanceolate leaves about three inches long, and white flowers. The red ovoid fruits have a sharp flavour and are sometimes used in making jellies. This species is often used for clipped hedges in California.

Callistemon speciosus [706] is one of the Australian **Bottle-brushes**. It is a tall shrub with narrow leaves which produces cylindrical groups of dark red flowers from May to July. The perianth is small and the numerous slender stamens project far beyond its edge. The fruit is a capsule with minute seeds.

707

708

Calothamnus sanguineus [707] is an evergreen shrub from western Australia. It has narrow leaves and attractive lateral clusters of red flowers.

Feijoa sellowiana [708] from Brazil is an evergreen shrub with opposite, dark green, ovate leaves. The flowers have white petals and red stamens. The ovoid berry is edible.

The 300 species of Australian **Gum Trees**, *Eucalyptus* spp., include the **Blue Gum**, *E. globulus* [709, 710], which attains a height of 200 feet. Species of Eucalyptus are cultivated in western North America and many other countries.

709

710

The *Melastomataceae* are a tropical family including at least 4,000 species of herbs, shrubs and trees. The opposite leaves are simple and have a characteristic palmate venation. The flowers are bisexual and the fruit is a berry or a capsule. *Medinilla venosa* [711] from Malaya has seven-nerved leaves which are rusty on the upper surface and small clusters of small pink flowers. *Sonerila margaritacea* [712] is a herb from south-east Asia with veined leaves which are purplish below and bear white spots on their upper surfaces. The flowers are pink. *Bertolonia × houtteana* [713] is a cultivated form with broad leaves and spikes of few flowers.

One of the two species included in the family *Punicaceae* is the **Pomegranate**, *Punica granatum* [coloured plate XIX]. It is a deciduous, spiny shrub or tree with obovate, shiny, opposite leaves. The orange-red, showy flowers have numerous stamens. The fruit is a spherical berry up to three inches across. The edible pulp of the fruit is formed from the fleshy coats of the numerous seeds.

711

712

713

XXIIIa   *Fritillaria imperialis* (**Crown Imperial**)

XXIIIb *Aspidistra lurida*

XXIV   *Gladiolus gandavensis*

714

The **Purple Loosestrife**, *Lythrum salicaria* [714], is a member of the cosmopolitan family *Lythraceae*. It is a perennial herb up to four feet high with lanceolate leaves and handsome spikes of purple flowers which are produced between June and August. The fruit is an ovoid capsule.

715

716

Most of the 500 species included in the family *Onagraceae* [715–719] are annual or perennial herbs although a few attain the dimensions of small trees. They are widely distributed in temperate regions and are particularly common in North and South America. The leaves are simple and the bisexual flowers often have four sepals and four petals. The ovary is always below the level of the other floral parts and the fruit is often a capsule. The family is of importance only for cultivated ornamental plants.

717

718

362

The **Rose-bay Willow-herb**, *Chamaenerion angustifolium* [715, 716], is widespread in north temperate regions particularly on stony or disturbed ground and in woodland clearings. It is a rhizomatous perennial up to four feet high with narrow, spirally arranged leaves. The terminal spikes of attractive flowers are produced between July and September. Each flower has four sepals, four rose-purple petals and eight stamens which shed their pollen before the four-armed stigma becomes receptive. The fruit [716] is a long narrow capsule with four valves which curve outwards, thus releasing the many small, white-plumed seeds.

The **Evening Primrose**, *Oenothera biennis* [717, 718], is a native of North America which has become widely naturalized in the British Isles, Europe and New Zealand. It is a biennial herb with erect stems up to three feet high and hairy, lanceolate leaves. The long yellow fragrant flowers are produced between June and September; they open in the evening and are pollinated by moths. The short cylindrical capsules [718] contain many minute seeds.

Most of the 80 species of *Fuchsia* are natives of tropical America. A number are cultivated but many of

719

the varieties grown are derived from *F. speciosa* [719], a hybrid between *F. magellanica* and *F. fulgens*.

The **Water Chestnut**, *Trapa natans* [720], is one of three species belonging to the family *Trapaceae*. It is a floating aquatic annual with diamond-shaped toothed leaves and a characteristic horned fruit.

720

721

722

The **Grape** family, *Vitaceae* [721–725], includes about 600 species, most of which occur in tropical areas although some extend into north and south temperate regions. They are nearly all climbing shrubs with tendrils and alternate leaves. The minute flowers are bisexual or unisexual and are borne in dense clusters opposite the leaves. The fruit is a berry containing few seeds.

The most important member of the family is the **Wine Grape**, *Vitis vinifera* [721, 722]. It has been in cultivation since ancient times and its origin is obscure but it is probably a native of the Caspian area of the Caucasus or western India. The tendrils are not as frequent as those of some other species and the thin leaves are deeply lobed and coarsely toothed. The green petals of the small flowers remain attached to each other apically and the whole corolla forms a cup which is shed to expose the five stamens and central gynoecium. The oval fruits are black when ripe. The **Parsley Vine**, var. *apiifolia*, has deeply dissected leaves. Dried currants are produced from the fruits of var. *corinthiaca*. There are probably from 60 to 70 species of *Vitis*, many of them natives of North America, but extensive cultivation together with much cross-breeding and grafting have made recognition of distinct species very difficult.

723

Parthenocissus tricuspidata [723, 724] is a native of China and Japan. It is a commonly grown, vigorous climber which attaches itself to supports by means of adhesive tips of the tendrils. Most of the leaves are trilobed and turn rich reds and browns in the autumn.

The true **Virginia Creeper** is *P. quinquefolia* [725], a native of eastern North America. It has branched tendrils and most of the leaves have five distinct, toothed, dull green leaflets. The globose fruits are black and about ¼ inch across.

724

725

The **Cashew** family, *Anacardiaceae*, includes about 600 species of widespread trees and shrubs. They mostly have opposite, compound leaves and small flowers in dense clusters. The fruit is usually succulent. It is of economic importance for such things as cashew nuts (*Anacardium*), mango (*Mangifera*) and lacquers (*Rhus* spp.)

The **Staghorn Sumach**, *Rhus typhina* [726], is a native of the eastern United States which is planted in towns because it can tolerate a smoky atmosphere. It reaches a height of 25 feet and has a broad crown and large alternate pinnate leaves. The trees are unisexual and the tiny flowers are borne in dense erect clusters. The flowers are greenish-yellow but the fruits are covered with red hairs.

Greyia sutherlandii [727] belongs to the small family *Melianthaceae*. It is an attractive South African species with toothed leaves and dense pyramidal spikes of flowers.

726

727

728

729

The important **Maple** family, *Aceraceae* [728–732], includes about 120 species all but two of which belong to the genus *Acer*. They are north temperate trees or shrubs with opposite leaves and small flowers. The fruit consists of two one-seeded portions.

Acer pseudoplatanus [728, 731] is a native of central Europe and western Asia but has been widely planted and has become naturalized in many countries including Britain where it is known as **Sycamore**, a name applied in America to *Platanus*

367

occidentalis. It is a deciduous
tree up to 100 feet high with a
smooth greyish-brown bark
and coarsely toothed, five-
lobed blades. The greenish-
yellow flowers are borne in
pendulous clusters [728]. Each
portion of the fruit has a stiff,
thin, brown wing [731]. Fruit
production is high and many
seedlings can be seen near
mature trees every spring.

The **Norway Maple**, *Acer
platanoides* [729, 730], has a
native range similar to that of
A. pseudoplatanus. It is often
planted in Britain and North
America but has not become
extensively naturalized. The
bark is fissured and the margin
of the leaf is rounded between
the lobes. The yellowish
flowers are borne in rounded
groups [730] and the wings of
the fruit [729] are widely
divergent.

730

731

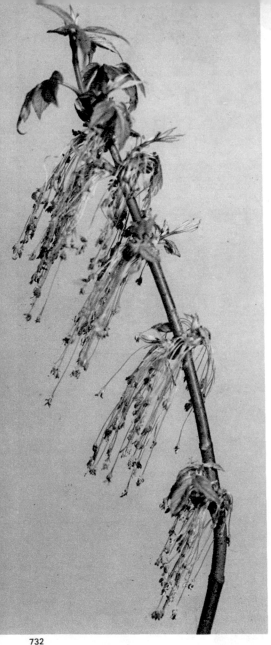

732

733

high with alternate pinnate leaves. The handsome erect groups of white flowers [733] appear in May. The top-shaped capsule [734] opens by three valves to release the dark brown seeds.

734

369

The **Box Elder.** *Acer negundo* [732], is widespread in North America. It is a tree up to 70 feet tall with a grooved bark and compound leaves. The yellowish-green flowers are unisexual and are borne in pendulous groups on separate trees. The sickle-shaped wings of the fruit are at an acute angle.

The **Soapberry** family, *Sapindaceae*, includes over 1,000 woody plants which are mainly tropical in distribution. *Xanthoceras sorbifolium* [733, 734], a native of China, is a deciduous shrub up to 20 feet

735

The family *Hippocastanaceae* [735–737] contains less than 30 species, all but two of which belong to the genus *Aesculus*.

A. hippocastanum [735–737], the **Horse-chestnut**, is a native of south-east Europe, Persia and the Hima-layas but has been widely planted in North America, Europe, and in the British Isles (where it is often found semi-wild). It is a large deciduous tree up to 100 feet high with arching branches and a thick trunk covered with a dark brown scaling bark. The

736

737

smooth twigs bear large brown sticky buds. The opposite pairs of leaves have long stalks and palmate blades with usually seven sharply toothed leaflets. The conspicuous, erect, conical groups of white flowers [735] appear during May. The four petals are marked with yellow spots which later turn pink. The projecting stamens are curved and the anthers contain red pollen. At the top of the inflorescence the flowers are male whereas those at the base are bisexual. The large green spherical fruit [736] has a thick leathery outer wall covered with thick spines. It is a capsule which breaks open to release the one or two large brown seeds [737].

A. carnea is a smaller tree with red or pink flowers. It is a fertile hybrid between the **Horse-chestnut** and the **Red Buckeye**, *A. pavia*. The latter, a native of the eastern United States, is a small tree rarely exceeding 15 feet in height with red flowers and smooth brown fruits. Several other North American species are known as **Buckeyes**.

738

The **Balsam** family, *Balsaminaceae* [738–741], includes about 450 species of herbs, most of which belong to the genus *Impatiens*. They are widely distributed but are particularly common in tropical regions of Africa and Asia. They are mostly soft herbs with translucent stems and simple leaves variously arranged. The showy, bisexual flowers are bilaterally symmetrical. One sepal has a backwardly projecting, nectar-secreting spur; the lower petals are larger than the upper ones. The five stamens form a hood surrounding the five-celled central ovary. The fruit is often a fleshy pendulous capsule which opens violently and forcibly ejects the seeds.

Touch-me-not, *Impatiens noli-tangere* [738], is found in wet places by streams and in woods throughout Europe and temperate Asia. It is also found in a few places in northern England. It is a smooth erect annual up to two feet high with alternate oblong toothed leaves. The flowers appear between July and September in small, slender-stalked axillary groups.

Impatiens balsamina [739, 740] is a native of India, Malaya and China which has been cultivated for many years. It is an annual about 18 inches high with oblong, deeply toothed leaves. The large flowers are often red but cultivated forms with varying colours and double flowers are known. The short cylindrical fruits [740] are green. *I. holstii* [741] from eastern tropical Africa is also often cultivated. It has reddish stems up to three feet high and ovate leaves with rounded teeth. This species is similar to *I. sultani* from Zanzibar and hybrids between the two are known. The **Jewel-weeds**, *I. capensis* and *I. pallida*, are familiar native North American species.

The **Chinese Dove Tree**, *Davidia involucrata* [742], is included in the small family *Nyssaceae*. It is a deciduous tree up to 50 feet high with alternate, ovate, toothed leaves. The small flowers are in a dense head which is surrounded by two large bracts up to six inches long. The genus *Nyssa* is North American, including *N. sylvatica*, the **Sourgum**.

741

742

743
744

The **Dogwood** family, *Cornaceae* [743–750], consists of about 90 species of widely distributed trees and shrubs. The leaves are usually opposite and simple. The flowers are bisexual or unisexual with a two- to four-celled ovary below the insertion of the other floral parts. The fruit is usually fleshy and contains one or two seeds. The family is of little economic importance except for the numerous ornamental shrubs it provides.

The **Cornel** or **Cornelian Cherry**, *Cornus mas* [743, 744], which occurs in central and southern Europe and western Asia, is a shrub or small tree attaining a height of 25 feet. It has pointed, ovate leaves about two inches long with three to five pairs of conspicuous veins. The small yellow flowers which appear in February before the leaves unfold are borne in dense clusters subtended by small, yellow, boat-shaped bracts. The fruit is a red ovoid berry [744]. The wood of this plant is very hard and is used in turnery. It is cultivated in North America.

The **Dogwood**, *Cornus sanguinea* [745, 746], is a native in England, Europe and south-west Asia and is found mainly in woods and scrub on calcareous soils. It is a deciduous shrub from one to 18 feet high with reddish purple twigs. The ovate leaves are about three inches long with three or four pairs of veins.

746

The crowded, flat-topped clusters of small whitish flowers appear in June and July. The calyx has very small teeth and the corolla has four pointed petals. The globose, shiny, black fruits [746] are ripe in the autumn at which time the foliage turns reddish-purple.

Cornus alba [747], a native of north-east Asia, is sometimes planted in gardens. It is a deciduous shrub up to 10 feet high with ovate leaves which are dark green above, whitish below and have six pairs of veins. The clusters of yellowish-white flowers appear in June and the globose fruit is white with a tinge of blue. A form with variegated leaves, var. *sibirica*, is sometimes cultivated. The **Red-Osier Dogwood**, *Cornus stolonifera*, from eastern North America, is a similar shrub but the leaves are larger and it produces prostrate, freely suckering stems. It has been widely planted in Britain and has become naturalized in places. The **Flowering Dogwood**, *Cornus florida* [748], is a native of the eastern United States. It is a deciduous shrub up to 20 feet high with ovate leaves about six inches long which are dark green above but paler and hairy underneath. The small flowers which appear in May are subtended by four white notched bracts about two inches long.

The widely planted **Spotted Laurel**, *Aucuba japonica* [749], is a native of Japan. It is a dense evergreen shrub up to 10 feet high with stout green twigs. The glossy leathery leaves are ovate to lanceolate, about eight inches long and are coarsely toothed towards the tip. On male plants the leaves are dark green but on female plants they are marked with yellow spots. The minute purplish flowers are produced in terminal clusters during April. The small fruit is red when mature.

747
748

749

Helwingia japonica [750], also from Japan, is a small deciduous shrub not more than four feet high. It has alternate, ovate leaves about three inches long with finely toothed margins. The minute male and female flowers are produced on different plants during May. The rounded fruit is about $\frac{1}{4}$ inch across.

750

The family *Araliaceae* [751–754] is a large tropical family with two main centres, tropical America and the India-Malaya area. It includes at least 700 species, most of which are trees, shrubs or woody climbers. The leaves are generally alternate and the small flowers, which are often borne in crowded inflorescences, have ovaries inserted below the level of the other floral parts. The fruit is often a succulent berry. The family is of little economic importance.

The common **Ivy**, *Hedera helix* [751, 752], occurs throughout the British Isles, Europe and Asia Minor and is widely planted in North America. It is a woody climber with small roots which enable it to cling securely to walls and tree trunks. It can attain a height of 50 feet or more, but may also be found creeping on the ground to form a thick carpet. The alternate, dark green leaves have relatively long stalks and the blades vary greatly in shape; on the creeping vegetative branches they are more or less palmately lobed but on the projecting flowering shoots they are ovate with entire margins.

Although the Ivy will grow successfully in deep shade, flowers are only produced on shoots exposed to light. They appear between September and November and are borne in globose clusters [751]. The flowers are small, with five yellowish triangular petals. They are pollinated by flies and wasps and the dull black rounded fruits [752] mature in the following spring. Although they have an emetic effect on human beings the berries are readily eaten by birds. There are numerous varieties, with deeply divided or variegated leaves.

751

752

379

Fatsia japonica [753] is an evergreen shrub from Japan which attains a height of 15 feet. It has thick smooth stems and large alternate leaves up to 16 inches long with broad, palmately lobed blades. The umbels of white flowers appear in October.

Several species of *Aralia* are cultivated in gardens, including *A. elata* [754] from north-east Asia. It has spreading pinnate leaves up to three feet long. Other species are native in North American woodlands, including *Panax quinquefolius.*

753

754

The **Carrot** family, *Umbelliferae*
[755–765], includes about 2,700
species, most of which are found
in north temperate regions. They
are mostly biennial or perennial
herbs with hollow stems and
large, alternate, compound or
dissected leaves. The leaf-stalks
are often long and have sheathing
bases. The inflorescence is a
simple or compound umbel
bearing many small flowers. The
latter are usually bisexual but
unisexual flowers occur in a few
species. The calyx is reduced to
five small teeth or a ridge, or is
absent. There are five petals, five
stamens and a two-celled ovary
below the insertion of the other
floral parts. The fruit, which is
very characteristic of the family,
splits into two one-seeded portions or mericarps. Various
detailed structures of the fruits
are important for identifying the
different genera.

The family is a natural group and
its members are easily distinguish-
able from those of other families.
It is important economically for
various food plants including
Carrot, Parsley, Parsnip and
Celery and for flavourings such
as Dill, Caraway, Anise and
Lovage. A number, including
Hemlock, are highly poisonous.

381

Hacquetia, *Hacquetia epipactis* [755], is a small perennial from four to 10 inches high which flourishes in light woods of the eastern Alps and Carpathians. It has palmately lobed leaves and the small circular umbels of yellow flowers, each surrounded by five spreading bracts, appear in April.

Masterwort, *Astrantia major* [756], grows in damp shady places at low elevations and on mountain pastures up to 6,500 feet, from Spain through southern and central Europe, to the Caucasus. Although not a native of the British Isles it has been cultivated for many years and has become naturalized in a few places. It is a perennial from one to three feet high with long-stalked, palmate, toothed blades. Flowering occurs between June and September and each umbel, from one to two inches across, is surrounded by from 15 to 20 greenish-pink bracts. The flowers have white or pink, notched petals. Most of the flowers are bisexual but some, particularly those produced late in the season, have no ovaries. The ovoid fruit has a number of toothed, vertical ridges.

757

758

759

382

The genus *Eryngium* includes over 200 species of
stiff, mostly spiny, perennial herbs found mainly in
temperate and subtropical regions of South America.
E. campestre [757] grows in dry places from southern
and central Europe to central Russia and also in
Persia and North Africa. It is a rare native of southern England and has been introduced into North
America. The erect, branched, pale green stems are
from one to two feet high. It has pinnate basal leaves
and deeply divided spiny stem-leaves. The small ovoid
heads of white or purplish flowers appear in July or
August.

The **Sea Holly**, *Eryngium maritimum* [758], occurs on
shingle and sand of the coasts of the British Isles,
western Europe, the Mediterranean and the Black
Sea. It is a glaucous green perennial from one to two
feet high with three-lobed basal leaves and palmate
stem-leaves, all having thick spiny margins. Each
ovoid head of pale blue flowers is about an inch long
and surrounded by from five to seven purplish,
spreading bracts with toothed, spiny margins. The
fruit is covered with small hooked bristles.

The **Small Bur-parsley**, *Caucalis platycarpos* [759], is
an erect annual up to a foot high. It is a native of
Europe and Western Asia occasionally found as a
weed on arable land in Britain. It has dissected leaves
and compound umbels of white or pink flowers. The
fruit bears rows of hooked spines.

762
763

Sweet Cicely, *Myrrhis odorata* [760], is a European plant of mountainous regions which is fairly common in hedges and woods of northern England and southern Scotland. The whole plant has a strong characteristic smell. It is a stout hairy perennial up to three feet high with soft, pinnately dissected leaves. The compound umbels of white flowers are about two inches across and appear in May and June. Some of the partial umbels bear only male flowers. The elongated fruits are beaked and strongly ridged. The name **Sweet Cicely** is applied in North America to an entirely different genus, *Osmorhiza*.

Orlaya grandiflora [761] occurs mainly in the Mediterranean region on calcareous soils. It is about three feet high and the umbels of white flowers appear in July and August. The petals of the marginal flowers, especially those towards the outside, are much larger than the central flowers of the umbel.

Caraway, *Carum carvi* [762], is widespread in Europe and Asia and is occasionally found in south-east England. It is a much-branched, erect, perennial up to two feet high. The leaf blades are triangular and deeply dissected. The umbels of small white flowers appear in June and July. The oblong fruits emit a strong smell when crushed.

Fennel, *Foeniculum vulgare* [763], appears to be a native of the Mediterranean region but has become widely naturalized in temperate countries including Britain where it occurs on waste places and sea cliffs. It is a smooth glaucous perennial up to five feet high which has much - divided leaves with linear segments. The umbels of yellow flowers appear between July and October and the fruits are ovoid. The whole plant has a characteristic strong smell.

The **Wild Carrot** or **Queen Anne's Lace,** *Daucus carota* [764], is a native throughout the British Isles, Europe and much of Asia and has become extensively naturalized in America and many other regions. It is an erect biennial up to three feet high with bristly stems and dissected leaves. The dense umbels of white flowers are seen from June to August. The ovoid fruits are covered with rows of hooked bristles. This is a very variable species; the cultivated **Carrot** is subsp. *sativus*.

Heracleum sphondylium [765], known as **Hogweed, Cow Parsnip** or **Keck**, is widespread in the British Isles, Europe and Asia and has been introduced into North America. It is a coarse hairy biennial up to six feet high with large umbels of white flowers and flattened fruits. *H. lanatum* is a native North American species.

764

765

The **Madder** family, *Rubiaceae*, includes about 5,000 species, most of which are tropical and subtropical trees or shrubs. The herbaceous **Bedstraws**, *Galium* spp., extend into temperate areas. The simple leaves are opposite or whorled and the small crowded flowers are bisexual. The two-celled ovary is below the insertion of the other floral parts. Several members of the family are of economic importance including coffee (*Coffea*) [coloured plate XXa] and quinine (*Cinchona*).

Myrmecodia echinata [766] is an interesting member of the family found in south-east Asia. It grows on other plants, attached by adventitious roots, and its base forms a swollen corky tuber. This is penetrated by a network of tunnels and galleries which are always inhabited by ants. It is doubtful whether the insects play any part in the life of the plant.

766

767

768

769

The **Honeysuckle** family, *Caprifoliaceae* [767–778], consists of about 300 species which are widespread but found particularly in north temperate regions. They are mainly shrubs and vines with opposite leaves and bisexual flowers. The five sepals are often small, the five petals are fused together and the five stamens are attached to the inside of the corolla tube. The two- to five-celled ovary is inserted below the level of the other floral parts. The family is important mainly for the large number of ornamental shrubs.

The **Elder**, *Sambucus nigra* [767, 768], occurs in woods, scrub and waste places throughout the British Isles, Europe, western Asia and North Africa. It is a shrub or small tree up to 30 feet high. Most of the leaves have from five to seven ovate leaflets. The small creamy-white flowers are produced in crowded, flat-topped clusters up to eight inches across, during June and July. The calyx is very small and the corolla, which is about $\frac{1}{4}$ inch across, has a short tube. The ovoid succulent fruit [768] is black when ripe.

770

The **Danewort**, *Sambucus ebulus* [769], occurs in central and southern Europe, the Mediterranean region and western Asia to the Himalayas. It is widely scattered although doubtfully native in the British Isles. It is a perennial, strong-smelling herb with creeping rhizomes and erect stems from two to four feet high. The pinnate leaves have from seven to 13 leaflets. The terminal clusters of small pinkish flowers are produced in July or August. The black fruit is spherical.

The **Guelder Rose**, *Viburnum opulus* [770–772], is found throughout most of the British Isles, all parts of Europe and northern and western Asia, particularly where the soil is damp, and is cultivated in North America. It is a deciduous shrub up to 18 feet high with a smooth greyish bark and five-lobed, coarsely toothed leaves. The loose, flattened clusters of flowers are from two to four inches across and appear in June and July. The small central flowers are fertile but the larger, white peripheral ones are sterile [770]. The succulent, sub-globose, red fruits are borne in pendulous clusters [772]. The **Snowball Tree**, which is often grown in gardens, is var. *roseum*. It has spherical clusters of large white sterile flowers [771].

773
774

The **Wayfaring Tree**, *Viburnum lantana* [773, 774], occurs in woods and hedges, particularly on calcareous soils in Britain, Europe, western Asia, Morocco, and has become naturalized in North America. It is a deciduous shrub up to 20 feet high with woolly twigs and buds unprotected by scales. The ovate, finely toothed leaves are about four inches long and are covered with dense hairs underneath. The crowded rounded clusters of small creamy-white flowers appear in May and June. The fleshy, ovoid fruits are green at first, then red and finally turn black when ripe. Frequently fruits at various stages of development can be found in the same cluster.

Many of the 120 species of *Viburnum* are frequently cultivated as ornamental shrubs. Among these is

V. rhytidophyllum [775], a native of central and western China. It is an evergreen shrub up to 10 feet high with erect hairy twigs and deeply wrinkled, lanceolate leaves about eight inches long. The large convex clusters of creamy-white flowers are produced in May and June. The fleshy fruits turn red and then black. Other species which are sometimes planted are the evergreen **Possum-hair** or **Swamp-hair**, *V. nudum*, from eastern North America, and **Laurustinus**. *V. tinus*, a deciduous shrub from the Mediterranean. All but one of the 15 species of *Symphoricarpos* are natives of North America. The **Snowberry**, *S. rivularis* [776], occurs naturally from Alaska and Alberta to California and Colorado. It is often planted and has become more or less naturalized in Britain. It is a spreading shrub up to 10 feet high with slender erect

stems and dull green more or less ovate leaves. The
small, bell-shaped, pink flowers are produced between March and July in crowded terminal groups.
The fruit is a soft, spherical white berry which ripens
between September and November.

The genus *Lonicera* includes about 180 species of
shrubs or woody climbers. The **Perfoliate Honeysuckle**, *L. caprifolium* [777], is a native of central and
southern Europe, western Asia and Asia Minor. It is
a twining shrub which has been introduced into
Britain and is found in hedgerows in a number of
places. Towards the top of the plant the opposite
leaves of each pair are joined, forming a continuous
collar round the stem. The terminal heads of few
flowers are produced in May and June. The long,
slender, bilaterally symmetrical corolla is creamy-
white at first but turns darker with age. It is pollinated
by hawk moths. The fruit is a red berry containing a
few seeds. The common **Honeysuckle** or **Woodbine**,
L. periclymenum, which is abundant in woods
throughout the British Isles and Europe and has
escaped from cultivation in North America, is a very
similar plant but none of the leaves are joined and the
bracts beneath the flowers are much smaller.

The genus *Weigela* includes a number of widespread
deciduous shrubs which are commonly cultivated for
their attractive white, pink or red flowers.

W. florida [778] is a native of China. It reaches a height
of seven feet and has hairy branches. The broadly
lanceolate leaves are toothed. The funnel-shaped
flowers which appear in May and June are deep pink
outside and much paler inside. The fruit is a capsule.

776

777

393

779

780

781

The **Valerian** family, *Valerianaceae*, includes about 350 species of herbs which are widely distributed except in Australia. The common **Valerian**, *Valeriana officinalis* [779], occurs throughout the British Isles and temperate Europe and Asia. It is a stout perennial up to five feet high with opposite pinnate leaves. The dense clusters of small, pale pink, bisexual flowers appear between June and August. Each flower has three stamens and a small basal ovary. The fruit contains a single seed and bears a terminal pappus of stiff-spreading hairs.

The **Scabious** family, *Dipsacaceae*, consists of about 150 species found mainly in the Near East and Mediterranean regions. The **Teasel**, *Dipsacus fullonum* [780, 781], is a biennial herb with stiff, erect, prickly stems up to six feet high. The large basal leaves are oblong but the smaller stem leaves are lanceolate. The ovoid heads of the purple flowers are over two inches long and appear in July and August. The dried heads of the cultivated **Fuller's Teasel**, subsp. *fullonum*, which have stiff, pointed, receptacular bracts, are used for raising the knap on cloth. The pale yellow **Scabious**, *Scabiosa ochroleuca* [782], is a European species which occurs on dry sunny slopes. It is a

782

783

perennial up to two feet high which flowers between June and October.

The **Convolvulus** family, *Convolvulaceae*, includes about 1,000 species, most of which are tropical herbs or shrubs. They are often climbers with alternate leaves, large bisexual flowers and capsular fruits.

The **Bellbine** or **Hedge Bindweed**, *Calystegia sepium* [783], is a variable perennial climbing plant widespread in north temperate regions. It has a creeping rhizome and long twining stems. The alternate leaves are heart-shaped and the solitary, white or pink flowers have a large funnel-shaped corolla. At the top of the flower stalk are large bracteoles which enclose the calyx and the spherical capsule.

The **Field Bindweed** or **Cornbine**, *Convolvulus arvensis* [784], is a widespread plant in the temperate regions and is often a troublesome weed of cultivated land. It is a perennial climber similar to *Calystegia sepium* but smaller in all its parts. The bracteoles are borne on the flower stalk some distance below the calyx.

784

785

786

The **Sweet Potato**, *Ipomoea batatas* [785], a native of
Central America, is now widely cultivated in the
tropics for its underground edible root.

The **Large Dodder**, *Cuscuta europaea* [786], is widespread in southern parts of the British Isles, Europe
and Asia and has been introduced into North
America. It is a non-green, annual, parasitic twining
plant found particularly on the **Stinging Nettle**,
Urtica dioica, and the **Hop**, *Humulus lupulus*. It has
slender reddish stems which are attached to the host
by suckers or haustoria. The small pinkish-white
flowers are in clusters and the capsule contains four
seeds. Many other Dodders occur in North America.

787

788

Most of the 265 species included in the **Phlox** family, *Polemoniaceae* [787–790], are natives of the western United States. They are mainly herbs although a few are shrubs or small trees. The bisexual flowers have five joined sepals, a well-developed corolla tube with five stamens inserted on it, and a three-celled ovary. The fruit is usually a capsule containing seeds.

Jacob's Ladder, *Polemonium coeruleum* [787], is widely distributed in the north temperate zone and is native on limestone hills of northern England. It is a perennial up to three feet high with pinnate leaves. The blue or white flowers are produced during June and July. (The American Jacob's Ladder is *P. reptans.*) *Phlox paniculata* [788] is the species from which many of our garden varieties of **Phlox** have been derived. *P. setacea* [789] is a small species grown on rockeries.

789

790

791

Cobaea scandens [790] with several large purple flowers is widely cultivated. *Romanzoffia unalasch-censis* [792], of the family *Hydrophyllaceae*, is a small annual of the Aleutian Islands with white flowers.

The **Borage** family, *Boraginaceae* [791, 793–800, 802], includes about 2,000 species which are widely distributed, and particularly abundant in the Mediterranean region and eastern Asia. They are herbs, shrubs or trees with simple, entire, mostly alternate leaves, and many are covered with stiff hairs. The flowers are usually bisexual and are generally borne on coiled axes. The calyx has five teeth and the funnel-shaped corolla bears five stamens on its inner surface. The ovary is lobed and the fruit often consists of four one-seeded nutlets. Apart from a number of species cultivated for ornament the family is of little economic importance.

Hound's Tongue, *Cynoglossum officinale* [791], occurs in dry grassy places in Britain, Europe and Asia and has probably been introduced into North America.

792

793

It is an erect biennial from one to three feet high with leaves covered on both sides with silky hairs. The groups of small, dull red flowers appear between June and August. The flattened nutlets are covered with short spines.

795

794

The **Tuberous Comfrey**, *Symphytum tuberosum* [793], is a perennial with thick tuberous rhizomes and erect bristly stems from one to two feet high. It has elliptical, pointed leaves and the coiled terminal spikes of yellowish-

399

796
797

white flowers appear in June and July. The flower has a tubular corolla and five pointed scales alternating with the stamens. It grows in wet woods in Britain, Europe and south-east Asia.

Rindera umbellata [794] is a native of south-east Europe. It is a perennial with a simple, hairy, erect stem from one to two feet high and long narrow leaves. The terminal clusters of reddish-yellow to dark brown flowers appear in May or June.

Borage, *Borago officinalis* [795], is a native of central Europe and the Mediterranean region, and is found as an escape from gardens in Britain and North America. It is a stiff, hairy annual from one to two feet high with ovate leaves and few-flowered terminal inflorescences. The flowers appear between June and August and have bright blue corollas with pointed lobes and deep purple anthers.

Anchusa officinalis [796] is a European plant found occasionally as a garden escape elsewhere. It is a perennial from one to two feet high with lanceolate, hairy leaves. The purple or bright blue flowers open in pairs on one-sided spikes between June and October.

The **Water Forget-me-not**, *Myosotis scorpioides* [797], occurs in wet places throughout the north temperate zone. It is a perennial from six to 18 inches high with slender stems and broadly lanceolate leaves. The flowers are produced between May and September on thin coiled stems.

798

The bright blue corolla has five scales closing the mouth of the tube. The nutlets are black and shiny. *Pulmonaria mollissima* [798] grows in meadows at mountain and subalpine elevations from central and southern Europe to central Asia. It is a perennial with stout hairy stems and bluish-violet flowers.

800

801

Nonnea pulla [799] is an annual found on calcareous grassland in central and southern Europe. It produces its dark red flowers between May and August.

The **Blue Gromwell**, *Lithospermum purpurocaeruleum* [800], occurs in scrub on calcareous soil in central and southern Europe and eastwards to the Black Sea and Asia Minor. It is a rare plant in Britain. It is a perennial up to two feet high with narrow leaves. The flowers, which appear in May and June, are reddish-purple when they open but later turn bright blue. A number of species of *Lithospermum* are attractive American wild flowers.

802

Viper's Bugloss, *Echium vulgare* [802], has a range similar to that of the **Blue Gromwell** but is commoner in Britain. It is a hairy biennial from one to three feet high with long dense spikes of flowers produced between June and August. The flowers are pink at first but turn purplish-blue.

The **Verbena** family, *Verbenaceae* [801, 803, 804], includes about 800 species of trees, shrubs and herbs, most of which have a tropical or subtropical distribution. The flowers are more or less bilaterally symmetrical and the fruit is usually fleshy. The **Garden Verbena**, *V.* × *hybrida* [801], is of hybrid origin. There are many varieties with colours ranging from white to deep purple. *Lantana camara* [803] from Jamaica is a prickly shrub from six to 10 feet high with heads of pink to orange flowers and round black fruits. *Clerodendrum thompsonae* [804] is an evergreen climber from tropical west Africa. It has smooth, ovate, pointed leaves and stalked clusters of attractive flowers. The large calyx is white and the corolla is crimson.

803
804

405

The **Mint** family, *Labiatae* [805–816], includes well over 3,000 species. They are predominantly herbs although a few are shrubs or small trees. The family is widely distributed; many members are native to the Mediterranean region, and many others to North America including Mexico. They usually have quadrangular stems and simple, opposite leaves. The flowers are solitary or in dense axillary whorls. They are bisexual and bilaterally symmetrical. The calyx is often five-lobed, the corolla is usually two-lipped and the four (or two) stamens are attached to the inside of the corolla tube. The four-celled ovary gives rise to a fruit of four one-seeded nutlets surrounded by the persistent calyx.

This is a very easily recognized family. Its main economic importance is for essential oils such as lavender and rosemary and for numerous ornamental species.

807

808

Bugle, *Ajuga reptans* [805], is common in damp and shady places throughout the British Isles, Europe and western Asia, and sometimes escapes from cultivation in North America. It is a small perennial herb with a rhizome and leafy, creeping stolons. The erect, unbranched stems are from four to 12 inches high and bear short-stalked, ovate leaves. The whorls of flowers are produced between May and July in the axils of the upper leaf-like bracts which are often purple-tinged. The bell-shaped calyx has five short teeth and the blue corolla has a large, three-lobed lower lip and a very small upper lip. The four stamens and the slender style project beyond the mouth of the corolla. The ovoid nutlets have reticulate markings.

Scutellaria pinnatifida [806] is a small species of **Skullcap** from Iran. It has pinnately lobed leaves and the flowers are borne in pairs. The calyx is two-lipped and closes over the fruit after flowering. The corolla is also two-lipped with small lateral lobes. America has many species of this genus.

Self-heal, *Prunella vulgaris* [807], occurs in non-acid grassland and waste places throughout the north temperate zone and Australia. It is a perennial herb with a thin creeping rhizome. The ascending stems are from two to 12 inches high and bear pairs of ovate, short-stalked leaves. The close whorls of flowers form a terminal cylindrical head which appears between June and September. The small flower has a reddish two-lipped calyx and a purple tubular corolla with a hooded upper lip and a spreading lower lip. The stamens lie under the upper lip, but they may be absent. The smooth, oblong nutlets are hidden by the closed lips of the calyx.

The **Large-flowered Hemp-nettle**, *Galeopsis speciosa* [808], occurs throughout Europe and in Siberia. It is also found in cultivated land throughout the British Isles, but is not common. It is a stout annual with hairy erect stems and ovate, toothed leaves. The flowers appear in dense whorls between July and September. The calyx has five fine teeth, and the pale yellow corolla has a compressed, hooded upper lip and a three-lobed lower lip which is more or less purple.

809

Molucella laevis [809] is a native of Asia Minor, Syria and Iraq, and can occasionally be found in Iran. It has ovate, round-toothed leaves and conspicuous spikes of curious flowers in which the calyx forms a large expanded green funnel with the small purple corolla at the bottom.

XXV *Crocus chrysanthus*

XXVIa *Cattleya labiata*

XXVIb *Cattleya hybrida*

The **White Deadnettle**, *Lamium album* [810, 811], is widespread from western Europe to the Himalayas and Japan; it is a common plant of hedgerows and waste places in Britain except the extreme north, and is found as an escape in north-eastern North America. It is a hairy perennial with a creeping rhizome and soft, erect, quadrangular stems up to two feet high which bears opposite pairs of toothed, ovate leaves. The flowers are produced in dense axillary whorls towards the top of the stems between April and December. The flower is about an inch long and has a calyx with five pointed teeth and a compressed whitish corolla. The black hairy anthers of the four epipetalous stamens lie beneath the upper hooded lip of the corolla. The lower corolla lip is divided into three lobes, the lateral ones being small and pointed. Pollination is by bumble bees and the four nutlets are smooth and black. Normally the flowers are lateral and bilaterally symmetrical. However, occasionally the tip of the stem produces a single terminal flower which is more or less radially symmetrical and has projecting stamens. Such a flower [810] is described as peloric. A similar phenomenon is sometimes found in other plants, for example, the foxglove and the toadflax.

There are about 40 species of *Lamium*. They are all herbs and include the **Red Deadnettle**, *L. purpureum*, a common annual weed of cultivation.

810

811

409

812

Clary, *Salvia sclarea* [812], is a native of southern Europe. It is a biennial from two to three feet high with stout hairy stems and pairs of broadly ovate leaves up to nine inches long. The flowers are produced in small distant whorls on the upper parts of the stems during August. The calyx has five spiny teeth and the two-lipped pale blue corolla has an arched upper lip and a spreading lower lip. The two stamens are hidden within the corolla.

Stachys recta [813] is a native of south-east Europe and the Caucasus. It is a hairy perennial with erect stems about two feet high and ovate to lanceolate leaves. Between six and 10 flowers are borne in each distant whorl of the inflorescence. The calyx is hairy and has five spiny teeth. The yellowish-white corolla has an erect upper lip and a large, lobed lower lip. There are about 200 species of *Stachys*, including the widespread **Hedge Woundwort**, *S. sylvatica*, and **Marsh Woundwort**, *S. palustris*.

Sweet Marjoram, *Majorana hortensis* [814], is a native of the Mediterranean region which has long been grown as a pot herb. Although commonly cultivated as an annual it is, in fact, a shrubby perennial from one to two feet high with pairs of hairy ovate leaves.

813

814

815
816

The small white or purplish flowers appear in June, borne in dense ovoid heads which are grouped into clusters of between three and five. The small oval nutlets are dark brown. The **Wild Marjoram**, *Origanum vulgare*, is found in dry pastures in the southern part of Britain, Europe and western Asia. **Crete Dittany**, *Origanum dictamnus* [815], is a small shrub with erect stems about a foot high. The broadly ovate, entire leaves are spotted and covered on both surfaces with a thick layer of woolly hairs. The drooping cylindrical heads of pink or purplish flowers are produced between June and August.

There are several species of **Wild Thyme**, *Thymus* spp. [816]. They are variable and it is often difficult to distinguish them. They are small aromatic shrubs with prostrate and erect stems and ovate to lanceolate leaves. The inflorescence is more or less condensed; the small flowers are rose-purple.

The **Nightshade** family, *Solanaceae* [817–835], includes over 2,000 species which are found mainly in tropical America although some extend into temperate regions. They may be herbs, shrubs or trees, with alternate leaves and bisexual flowers. Both the calyx and corolla are commonly five-lobed and the five stamens are inserted on the corolla tube. The ovary is two-celled and the fruit, which is usually surrounded by the persistent calyx, is either a capsule or a berry. The family is of considerable economic importance for food plants such as potato, tomato and red pepper. Tobacco (*Nicotiana*) is included, as well as a number of highly poisonous plants, Henbane for example, from which valuable drugs are obtained. A large number of species are also grown as ornamental plants.

818

819

The **Potato**, *Solanum tuberosum* [817], is a native of the high valleys of Mexico, Peru and Chile. It was introduced into Europe about 1565; since that time many varieties have been produced and it is now one of the most important temperate food crops. It has soft, green, erect stems from two to three feet high, and irregularly pinnate leaves. The flattened corolla is white to purple and has yellow or orange anthers. The fruit (rarely formed) is a spherical, yellow or purple berry. The leaves, stems and fruit contain a poisonous alkaloid, solanin. A trace of this is present in the swollen underground stem tubers but is destroyed on cooking.

The **Tomato**, *Lycopersicum esculentum* [818], is also a native of South America from which a large number of cultivated varieties have been developed. They vary greatly in habit, but usually have dissected leaves and loose axillary clusters of yellow flowers. The fruit is a berry rich in vitamin C.

Bittersweet or **Woody Nightshade**, *Solanum dulcamara* [819], is widespread in woods and hedges throughout the British Isles, Europe, Asia and North America. It is a scrambling, woody perennial with entire or lobed leaves. The flowers, which appear in loose clusters between June and September, have purple corollas and yellow anthers forming a cone around the gynoecium. The fruit is a red ovoid berry. The **Black Nightshade**, *Solanum nigrum*, an annual up to two feet high with white flowers and black fruits, is a garden weed.

Capsicum annuum [820, 821], **Red** or **Cayenne Pepper** or **Chili**, is a variable annual unknown in the wild state. It is from one to six feet high with ovate, entire leaves, and white or greenish-white flowers. The fruit is a more or less dry berry with numerous seeds contained in two or three cavities. The fruits vary greatly in size, and are used in the green state or when they have ripened and turned red. The small forms have the strongest taste and are dried and ground as pepper. The **Long Cayenne**, var. *acuminatum*, is a much-branched plant about two feet high with narrow fruits about three inches long. The cultivated varieties with large fruits having a firm, thick flesh and a mild flavour are derived from var. *grossum*, a slightly branched form. They are eaten either green or red. Var. *abbreviatum* has small fruits about two inches long which are sometimes used for pickling, but this variety is more often grown for ornamental purposes only.

820

821

415

Although called the **Chinese Lantern**, *Physalis franchetii* [822, 823], is in fact a native of Japan which was first brought to Europe towards the end of the 19th century. It is usually a perennial but its duration of life appears to be variable. It has a creeping rhizome, simple erect stems up to two feet long and large, ovate, long-stalked leaves. The small, solitary, axillary flowers are white with yellow anthers. The fruit is a spherical red berry containing many seeds, surrounded by the large, inflated, orange-red calyx [822]. *P. alkekengi* from the Caucasus to China is a similar but smaller species.

822
823

The **Deadly Nightshade**, *Atropa bella-donna* [824, 825], occurs in woods and scrub on calcareous soils in central and southern Europe, western Asia and North Africa. It is a rare plant on chalk and limestone in England and Wales. It is a much-branched perennial herb about five feet high with ovate, pointed, entire leaves up to eight inches long borne alternately or in unequal pairs. The axillary pendulous flowers [825] are over an inch long; they appear between June and August. The calyx has five pointed lobes; the dull greenish - purple corolla is bell - shaped. The fruit [824] is a shiny black berry containing numerous seeds and is subtended by the spreading calyx. This is an extremely poisonous plant and, if eaten by a child, a single berry can rapidly cause death. It contains the alkaloids atropine and hyoscyamine, which are used medicinally.

824

825

417

826

827

Henbane, *Hyoscyamus niger* [826, 827], occurs in Europe, western Asia, North Africa and North America. It is a native of southern England and southeast Ireland but is found scattered throughout the British Isles in sandy places, particularly near the sea. It is an annual, or more commonly a biennial, sticky, hairy and with a pungent odour. The stiff stems are up to two feet high and bear alternate, oblong or ovate, coarsely toothed leaves. The flowers are nearly an inch across and are borne in two rows in the axils of leafy bracts on terminal inflorescences between June and August. The calyx has sharp teeth and the bell-shaped corolla is yellow with purple veins. The fruit, which is a round capsule, is constricted about the middle and is enclosed by the stiff persistent calyx [827]. The capsule opens by means of a lid to release the numerous tiny seeds. This is a very poisonous plant and contains the alkaloids hyoscyamine and scopolamine.

The **Thorn-apple** or **Jimson-weed**, *Datura stramonium* [828, 829], occurs widely in temperate and subtropical areas of the northern hemisphere. In Britain it is found occasionally more or less naturalized in waste places, and in the United States it is a common weed. It has erect green stems up to three feet high and large, ovate, coarsely toothed leaves which are arranged alternately. The erect, solitary flowers [829] are from two to three inches long, and appear between July and October. The pale green, angled calyx has narrow teeth, and the white or purple trumpet-shaped corolla has five pointed, more or less erect lobes. The stamens are inserted within the corolla tube. The fruit [828] is an ovoid capsule about two inches long, usually covered with long sharp spines and subtended by the persistent basal part of the calyx. The capsule wall opens by four valves. This is a very poisonous plant and contains the alkaloids hyoscine, hyoscyamine and scopolamine.

828

829
830

419

831

832

Scopolia carniolica [830] from western Asia is a perennial herb about a foot high, with broadly lanceolate leaves and solitary, pendulous flowers. The corolla is greenish-red and the fruit is a capsule included within the persistent calyx.

Nicotiana tabacum [831] is a native of tropical America which has been cultivated from earliest times for the tobacco prepared from its dried leaves. It is a stout viscid annual or biennial up to six feet high. The large, thin, alternate leaves are lanceolate to ovate, and their bases clasp the stem. The small pinkish flowers are borne in dense, stalked, drooping clusters. The calyx has five unequal teeth and the corolla is covered on the outside with woolly hairs. The five stamens are unequal, and included within the corolla tube. The ovary is two-celled, and the fruit is a

capsule which opens by valves to release the numerous roughened seeds. There are many varieties of this important plant, including var. *angustifolia* with narrow leaves and var. *macrophylla* with large leaves and large red flowers.

Nicotiana rustica [832] is a native of Mexico and Texas. It is a slender annual or biennial about three feet high with ovate or oblong stalked leaves. The yellowish-green flowers are about ¾ inch long, and are borne in dense clusters between July and September. This was the first species of tobacco introduced into Europe, probably towards the end of the 16th century. There are about 45 species in the genus *Nicotiana*. Several are cultivated for their large strongly-scented flowers, which open usually at night. The flowers of the two species illustrated here open during the day.

420

834

835

There are about 12 species of *Petunia*, all natives of South America. They are annual or perennial, viscid herbs with small entire leaves and large solitary flowers. The calyx is five-toothed and the funnel-shaped corolla is purple or white. Five stamens are attached to the corolla tube but in some species one of these is sterile. Most of our present-day **Garden Petunias**, *P. hybrida* [833, 834], appear to be derivatives of a single cross between *P. nyctaginiflora*, a species with white flowers, and the purple-flowered *P. integrifolia*. Subsequent selection has produced a large number of striped, fringed and double forms.

The genus *Brunfelsia* includes about 25 species of evergreen shrubs which are natives of South America and the West Indies. They have narrow, entire leaves and an abundance of sweetly scented flowers. The corolla has five spreading lobes, the stamens are enclosed within the corolla tube, and the fruit is a berry. *B. calycina* is an extremely variable species from Brazil, one recognized variety being var. *eximia* [835]. This is a slightly downy plant about two feet high with dark green leaves. The flowers, which appear between January and July, are about two inches across. They are deep purple at first, but later turn white.

836

The **Snapdragon** family, *Scrophulariaceae* [836–851], consists of about 3,000 species and is very widely distributed. Most of the members are herbs but a few are small shrubs or non-green parasites. The two, four or five stamens of the bisexual flowers are attached to the base of the corolla, which is almost always bilaterally symmetrical. The ovary is two-celled and the fruit is usually a capsule. Although large, the

837

838

family is of little economic importance except for numerous ornamental species.

Verbascum thapsiforme [836] is a native of central Europe. It is a biennial densely covered with white woolly hairs. It has large ovate-lanceolate leaves and in its second year the long terminal flowering spike reaches a height of six feet. Each flower has a yellow, flat, five-lobed corolla and five stamens. The fruit is an ovoid capsule containing many small seeds.

Most of the 200 species of *Calceolaria* [837] are natives of Chile and Peru, some extending as far north as Mexico. The many herbaceous varieties which are so popular with gardeners as bedding and pot plants are mainly derived from hybrids between two species from Chile, *C. arachnoidea* with small, dull purple flowers, and *C. crenatiflora* with yellow, brown-spotted flowers.

Toadflax, *Linaria vulgaris* [838], is common in grassy and waste places throughout much of the British Isles, Europe and Asia and has been introduced into North America. It is a perennial with a creeping rhizome, and erect stems up to two feet high which bear many narrow leaves. The crowded terminal spikes of yellow flowers appear between July and October. Each flower has a calyx with five teeth and a bilaterally symmetrical corolla with a narrow basal spur and two lips which hide the four stamens within. The ovoid ovary is two-celled and gives rise to a capsular fruit which opens apically to release the many minute seeds.

XXVIIa *Brassocattleya*

XXVIIb *Dendrobium nobile*

XXVIII *Odontoglossum grande*

The **Snapdragon**, *Antirrhinum majus* [839], is a native of the Mediterranean which has become naturalized in England and central Europe. The wild plant usually has a reddish-purple corolla but cultivated forms vary greatly in colour and habit.

Antirrhinum asarina [840] is a viscid, greyish, procumbent perennial found among rocks on mountains of south-west Europe. The small, solitary, white flowers are tinged red.

839

840

425

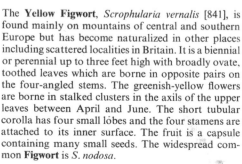

841

842

The **Yellow Figwort**, *Scrophularia vernalis* [841], is found mainly on mountains of central and southern Europe but has become naturalized in other places including scattered localities in Britain. It is a biennial or perennial up to three feet high with broadly ovate, toothed leaves which are borne in opposite pairs on the four-angled stems. The greenish-yellow flowers are borne in stalked clusters in the axils of the upper leaves between April and June. The short tubular corolla has four small lobes and the four stamens are attached to its inner surface. The fruit is a capsule containing many small seeds. The widespread common **Figwort** is *S. nodosa*.

The **Monkey-flower**, *Mimulus guttatus* [842], is a native of North America from Alaska and Montana to north-western Mexico, but it has become extensively naturalized in Europe and throughout the British Isles where it is often found on the banks of streams. It is a perennial, usually about a foot high with ovate, irregularly toothed leaves. The terminal groups of flowers appear between July and September. The calyx is five-toothed and the two-lipped yellow corolla is marked with small red spots. There are four stamens attached to the inner surface of the corolla tube. The ovoid capsule contains many seeds and is enclosed within the persistent inflated calyx.

The **Germander Speedwell**, *Veronica chamaedrys* [843], is native throughout the British Isles, Europe and northern and western Asia and has become naturalized in North America. It is a small perennial with weak ascending stems up to 15 inches high and ovate toothed leaves. The slender flowering spikes are produced in the axils of the upper leaves from March until July. Each flower is about ½ inch across and has a four-lobed calyx, a bright blue unequally four-lobed corolla marked with darker lines, and two stamens attached to the short corolla tube. The fruit is a flattened, heart-shaped capsule containing several seeds.

The **Rock Speedwell**, *V. fruticans* [844], is an arctic-alpine plant which occurs in Greenland, Iceland and Scandinavia, and on the mountains of Scotland and central and southern Europe. It is a shrubby perennial from two to six inches high with pairs of small thick leaves. The terminal groups of bright blue flowers are produced between July and September. This is a variable species, its stature depending upon the habitat.

843

844

427

845

846

There are about 20 species of **Foxgloves**, *Digitalis* spp., all of which are poisonous plants owing to the presence of the alkaloid digitalin, which is extracted from some species for medicinal purposes. The **Yellow Foxglove**, *D. grandiflora* [845], grows in woods on calcareous soils in Europe and western Asia. It is a biennial or short-lived perennial about three feet high with broadly lanceolate clasping leaves and long spikes of yellow brown-spotted flowers. The flower has a five-lobed calyx and a tubular corolla with four stamens attached to its inner surface. The capsule contains many minute seeds. The common **Foxglove**, *D. purpurea* [846], is a similar plant with pinkish-purple spotted or white flowers produced between June and September. It occurs widely in western Europe and throughout the British Isles particularly in woodland clearings and on dry heaths, and is extensively naturalized in north-western North America. *D. ferruginea* [848] occurs on stony slopes in south and south-east Europe and Asia Minor. It is a perennial from four to six feet high with smooth leaves and long dense spikes of rusty-red flowers.

The **Eyebrights**, *Euphrasia* spp. [847], are very small annual herbs widespread in temperate regions. The common British and European plants formerly included under *E. officinalis* have now been separated into a number of species. They generally grow in grassy places and have small opposite leaves. The flowers are white or purple with various markings.

847

848

849

850

851

Rhinanthus pulcher [849] grows in alpine and subalpine meadows in the Sudeten mountains and the Carpathians. It is an annual up to eight inches high with pairs of opposite, lanceolate, toothed leaves. The dense terminal clusters of yellowish flowers appear in July and August. Both the calyx and bilabiate corolla are laterally compressed. The capsule contains a few winged seeds. *Pedicularis oederi* [850] is a widespread arctic-alpine perennial with green pinnate leaves, semi-parasitic on the roots of other plants. The dense terminal groups of yellow flowers appear between June and August. The fruit is an elongated capsule containing few seeds. The **Red-rattle** or **Lousewort**, *P. palustris* [851], occurs in wet grassy places throughout the British Isles, Europe and western Asia. It is a semi-parasitic annual up to two feet high with oblong lobed leaves and purplish-pink flowers produced between May and September. The compressed curved capsule is longer than the calyx and contains a few large seeds. The genus *Pedicularis* includes a number of North American species.

Most of the 750 species belonging to the family *Bignoniaceae* [852–856] are tropical trees, shrubs or vines found mainly in northern South America. They usually have opposite, simple or pinnate leaves and showy, bisexual, bilaterally symmetrical flowers. The corolla is more or less funnel-shaped and has two or, more usually, four stamens attached to its inner surface. The two-celled ovary usually develops into a capsular fruit containing winged seeds. The family is of economic importance for a number of timber trees and tropical ornamentals such as the Jacaranda and Paulownia.

852
853

854

855

Campsis radicans [852], from North America, climbs by means of numerous aerial roots. It has pinnate leaves with ovate, toothed leaflets. and the large, orange-red. trumpet-shaped flowers are borne in terminal clusters during August and September. The **Indian Bean Tree** or **Catalpa**, *Catalpa bignonioides* [853–855], is a native of the eastern United States. It is a deciduous tree up to 50 feet

856
857

high with a dense, spreading crown. The broad, ovate leaves, which are often grouped in threes, are about eight inches long; they produce an unpleasant smell when bruised. The large clusters of trumpet-shaped flowers [853] are produced in July. The corolla is up to $1\frac{1}{2}$ inches long, white with yellow and purple spots. The long narrow fruits [854] are podlike and about 15 inches long. They contain numerous seeds which have a tuft of white hairs at each end [855]. This is an attractive ornamental tree and there are several cultivated varieties including var. *aurea* with yellow leaves. Another **Catalpa**, called also **Catawba** or **Cigar-tree**, *C. speciosa*, is a similar tree which reaches a height of 100 feet. It has longer narrow leaves and larger fruits. It is a very quick-growing tree and is often planted in the United States for its valuable, durable wood.

Incarvillea grandiflora [856] is one of the **Trumpet Flowers** which comes from western China. It is a dwarf perennial not more than 18 inches high with pinnate leaves. The flowers, which are from three to four inches across, pale red with a white throat, appear in May and June. Two other similar species, *I. compacta*, a dwarf plant, and the vigorous *I. delavayi*, are sometimes cultivated.

433

858

There are about 20 species of *Acanthus*, **Bear's Breeches**, most of which are natives of the Mediterranean region. *A. mollis* [857] is a herbaceous perennial from three to four feet high with leaves about two feet long and one foot across which have deeply indented margins. The loose terminal spikes of flowers up to 18 inches long are produced during the summer. Each white or rose-pink flower is subtended by a deeply toothed bract. There are a number of cultivated forms including var. *niger* with shiny green leaves and purple-white flowers.

The large tropical family *Acanthaceae* [857-861] includes well over 2,000 species which occur mainly in northern South America, Africa and the Indo-Malayan region. A wide range of habit is found but many are perennial herbs with opposite, simple leaves. The bisexual, bilaterally symmetrical flowers are borne singly or in dense inflorescences with well-developed bracts. The two or four stamens are attached to the corolla and the ovary is two-celled. The fruit is usually a capsule which opens violently by means of two valves. The family is of little economic importance except for a few species which are grown for decoration.

859

Another species which is sometimes grown is *A. spinosus*,
with pinnatifid spiny leaves
and dense spikes of purplish
flowers. It is believed that the
leaves of this plant, and probably also those of *A. mollis*,
were used as patterns for the
conventionalized decorations
on the capitals of Corinthian
columns.
Fittonia argyroneura [858] is
one of three species of herbaceous perennials native to
Peru. It is often grown in hothouses for its beautiful heart-
shaped, velvety leaves with
conspicuous white veins. It is
a small plant little more than
six inches high with erect
spikes of flowers subtended by
overlapping ovate bracts.

860

861

Jacobinia carnea [859] is a
native of Brazil. It has opposite, downy, lanceolate leaves
up to a foot long. Flowers are
produced when it is about two
feet high but it will grow much
taller if it is not cut. The
pinkish-purple flowers are
produced in handsome erect
inflorescences. Each flower
has a hooded upper lip, two
fertile stamens, and a down-
ward-curving lower lip.
Beloperone guttata [860] from
Mexico has weak stems from
two to three feet long and soft
ovate leaves. The insignificant
flowers are borne in drooping
clusters and are almost hidden
by the large reddish-brown,
heart-shaped bracts.
Daedalacanthus nervosus [861]
is a shrub of the East Indies
from two to six feet high. It
has ovate leaves and terminal
spikes of blue, two-lipped
flowers about an inch across.

435

The family *Gesneriaceae* [862-867] includes about 1,200 species which are widespread in tropical and subtropical regions. They are mostly herbs or shrubs with opposite hairy leaves. The showy bisexual flowers are bilaterally symmetrical with two or four stamens attached to the corolla. The ovary is one-celled and the fruit is usually a capsule containing many small seeds. The family is mainly important for the large number of ornamental species which are often grown in glasshouses in temperate countries.

Ramondia nathaliae [862] occurs on mountains in Bulgaria and Serbia. It is a perennial with a rosette of ovate, corrugated, glossy green leaves. The flowers are borne singly on long stalks. Each has a four-toothed calyx and a four-lobed corolla which ranges in colour from white to pale mauve with an orange centre. The fruit is a capsule containing many seeds.

862
863

The genus *Haberlea*, which is closely allied to *Ramondia*, embraces a single species, *H. rhodopensis* [863], confined in nature to a small rocky area of Thrace. It is a small, softly hairy perennial with thick, leathery ovate leaves from two to three inches long. The flowering stems are produced in April, each being about six inches long and bearing from two to five flowers. The calyx is five-toothed, and the pale mauve corolla has five unequal lobes. The four stamens are included within the corolla tube. A white-flowered form, var. *virginalis*, is also known.

The **African Violét**, *Saintpaulia ionantha* [865], grows near sea level in eastern tropical Africa. It is a small hairy perennial with many thin, stalked, ovate, slightly toothed leaves. Between one and six flowers are borne on each erect axillary stem. The flower has a deeply-lobed calyx and a two-lipped violet-blue, pink, or white corolla about an inch long. There are two stamens and the hairy ovary gives rise to a capsule containing many small seeds. Several cultivated varieties with different-coloured flowers are commonly grown.

S. kewensis [864] is a similar species with many white hairs on the surface of the leaves.

The genus *Achimenes* from tropical America, for example *A. erecta* [866], probably includes about 40 species, but repeated hybridization has obscured the specific limits in cultivated stocks. They are erect plants with opposite, hairy leaves and underground, scaly, cone-like tubers. The flowers have tubular corollas with spreading lobes. The genus is closely allied to *Isoloma*.

About 150 years ago a plant was introduced into England from Brazil under the name *Gloxinia speciosa*. It caused much interest and from it all our showy **Gloxinias** are derived. However, this plant really belongs to the genus *Sinningia*; its correct name is *S. speciosa* [867]. It differs from the true *Gloxinia* spp. in having a tuberous rhizome and five separate glands instead of a ring at the base of the ovary. The original species had small, drooping, uniformly purple flowers but as a result of continuous selection a large number of forms have been produced varying in colour, shape and size of the flower.

866
867

Orobanche lutea [868] is a **Broomrape** belonging to the family *Orobanchaceae*. There are about 100 species and they are all non-green total parasites attached to the roots of other plants. The erect scaly stems terminate either in dense spikes of dull-coloured, bisexual flowers or in single flowers.

Of the 250 species of insectivorous herbs belonging to the family *Lentibulariaceae* about 30 are included in the genus *Pinguicula*. The **Alpine Butterwort**, *P. alpina* [869], is a small perennial plant with an arctic-alpine distribution. The long thick root is crowned with a rosette of elliptical leaves which are covered with sticky hairs. Insects which get caught on these hairs are entombed by the slow inrolling of the leaf margin, and their bodies are broken down by digestive juices. The creamy-white flowers are borne singly on leafless erect stalks from May to August. The two-lipped corolla has a short spur and there are only two stamens. The ovoid capsule contains many small seeds.

The **Plantain** family, *Plantaginaceae* [870–872], includes about 200 species of herbs which are found mainly in temperate regions. The **Ribwort** or **Buckhorn**, *Plantago lanceolata* [870], is a native of Britain, Europe and northern and central Asia; it has been introduced as a weed of cultivation into most temperate countries. It has a rosette of spirally arranged narrow leaves up to a foot long. The small flowers appear between April and August in dense cylindrical heads borne terminally on long, leafless, unbranched stems. The wind-pollinated flower has an inconspicuous brown corolla and projecting stamens.

869
870

The ovoid fruit opens by a transverse slit to release the two seeds. The **Hoary Plantain**, *P. media* [871], has elliptical leaves and long narrow inflorescences. The filaments of the stamens are purple and the flowers are insect-pollinated. The fruit usually contains four seeds. *P. indica* [872] is a branched annual from south and central Europe and south-west Asia.

871

872

873
874

The **Flowering Rush** family, *Butomaceae* [873, 874], includes about nine species of perennials which grow in water or wet places. The **Flowering Rush**, *Butomus umbellatus* [873], is native in the southern parts of Britain, in Europe and in temperate Asia. It has also become naturalized in North America on the shores of the St Lawrence River and Lake Champlain, and elsewhere. It is a rhizomatous plant up to five feet high found growing on the margins of ditches, ponds and rivers. The long linear leaves are erect and pointed. The umbels of stalked flowers are borne at the ends of erect unbranched stems from July to September. The outer three perianth parts are small and sepal-like, the inner three larger and pink. There are from six to nine stamens and about the same number of almost separate carpels. The fruit consists of a group of follicles each containing numerous small seeds.

Hydrocleis nymphaeoides [874] is one of three species of aquatic plants from tropical South America. It is a floating herb having leaves with long stalks and ovate blades. The flowers have numerous stamens but the outer ones are sterile.

The *Hydrocharitaceae* is a family of about 70 species of completely or partially submerged aquatics, most of which are confined to warmer climates. Habit is variable. The flowers are usually unisexual. The perianth is in two whorls and the unilocular ovary in the female flower is below the insertion of the other floral parts.

The **Frog-bit**, *Hydrocharis morsus-ranae* [875], occurs in Europe and Asia and is found in ponds and ditches in scattered localities of England and Wales. It is a floating herb with groups of long-stalked

leaves having smooth, rounded blades. The flowers, which are produced singly on stalks and project above the water in July and August, have three small sepals and three white, crumpled petals. The male flower has 12 stamens, some of them sterile (staminodes). Staminodes are also present in the female flower. The fruit is fleshy.

Water Soldier, *Stratiotes aloides* [876], occurs in Europe and north-west Asia and in a few localities in Britain. It is a floating herb with a rosette of thick, spiny, stiff, aloe-like leaves up to 18 inches long. When the white flowers are produced between June and August the plants float at the surface, whereas at other times they sink. The male flowers are borne in small groups and have 12 stamens and numerous staminodes. The female flowers are solitary.

443

877

Canadian Pondweed, *Elodea canadensis* [877], is a native of North America. It is a submerged, branched aquatic with whorls of dark green simple leaves. When introduced into Britain about 1836 it spread rapidly but has since diminished.

The **Lily** family, *Liliaceae* [878–921, coloured plates XXI, XXIII], includes about 2,500 species of herbs which are widely distributed and diverse in habit. The flowers are bisexual and generally have petaloid perianth parts in two whorls, six stamens, and a

878

three-celled ovary. The fruit is a capsule or berry. Economically the family is important for asparagus, onions and many showy ornamental species.

Veratrum lobelianum [878] grows in wet places on the mountains of central and southern Europe. It is a perennial with a short thick rhizome, erect stems from two to three feet high, and large sheathing stems. The large terminal inflorescence of small green flowers appears between July and September. The plant is poisonous, as are the similar North American species.

445

879

Uvularia grandiflora [879] is a North American species with a creeping rhizome and smooth, translucent, oblong, alternate leaves from two to four inches long. Up to three pale yellow flowers are borne on each erect stem. They are up to 1½ inches long and have narrow perianth segments. The fruit is a capsule.

The **Meadow Saffron**, *Colchicum autumnale* [880], occurs in damp meadows in England and Wales and central and southern Europe. It has an underground corm which produces several narrow pointed leaves in the spring. The solitary pale purple flowers appear between August and October. The ovary is below ground, and the mature capsule does not appear until the following spring. This is often cultivated in the United States.

The **St Bruno's Lily**, *Paradisia liliastrum* [881], is a native of southern Europe. It has a short rhizome with thick, clustered roots and long, narrow leaves from one to two feet long in groups of from six to eight. The erect stems are about the same length as the leaves, and bear a loose spike of white, translucent, bell-shaped flowers each about two inches long.

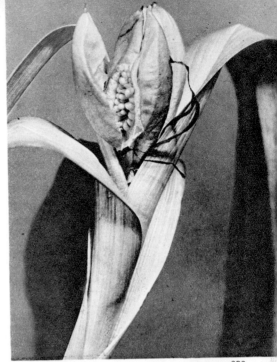

880

881

882

Eremurus robustus [882] is a stout perennial from Turkestan. It has bright green leaves from two to five feet long and up to four inches wide. The handsome spikes of the many peach-coloured flowers, which appear in June, can often reach a height of nine feet or even more.

448

883

Hosta ventricosa (= *Funkia ovata*) [883], from eastern Asia, has heart-shaped leaves up to nine inches long.

Groups of from 10 to 15 lavender-blue flowers appear in June.

449

The genus *Anthericum* includes about 50 species which are found in Europe, Asia and tropical and subtropical Africa. *A. liliago* [884] from southern Europe has a basal rosette of narrow, channelled leaves which are from 12 to 16 inches long. The erect, unbranched, flowering stems up to two feet long appear in the summer. They bear a few white flowers up to 1½ inches across, with narrow spreading segments and a curved style. The fruit is a capsule containing few seeds.

The **Day-lilies** belong to the genus *Hemerocallis* of which there are about 12 species in temperate eastern Asia. They have linear, grass-like leaves in two rows and numerous large yellow to reddish-orange flowers. The individual flowers only last for one or two days but as a large number are produced there is a long flowering period. *H. lilio-asphodelus* [885] is probably a native of China which has been in cultivation for many years. It is a vigorous plant which spreads underground and has narrow arching leaves up to two feet long. The fragrant, lemon-yellow flowers are three inches across and are borne on a closely branched inflorescence over three feet high. This is a variable species and the common cultivated form is propagated vegetatively because it does not set viable seed.

A hybrid day-lily has run wild and become very common on roadsides in north-eastern United States.

Phormium is a genus of two species called the **New Zealand Flax**. *P. tenax* [886] has a dense basal rosette of hard, tough, dark green leaves up to eight feet long and four or five inches wide. They have white or yellow margins and taper to a sharp point. The flowers are dull red, up to $2\frac{1}{2}$ inches long, and are borne in a large cluster from five to 16 feet high during the summer. The fruit is a straight capsule. This is an extremely variable species with both dwarf and variegated forms. The leaf fibres are very strong and are used for the same purposes as manilla or sisal hemp. It has been cultivated on a commercial scale in central India and the River Plate area of South America, and small quantities have been grown in Southern Ireland. The other species, *P. colensoi*, is a smaller but hardier species with yellow flowers on erect inflorescences from three to six feet high. The fruit is a long twisted capsule.

Although several species of *Agapanthus* have been described, they are all probably referable to the single variable *A. umbellatus* [888], the **African Lily** or **Lily-of-the-Nile**, a native of South Africa. The thick, narrow leaves are two feet long and the terminal cluster of from 10 to 30 blue, funnel-shaped flowers is borne on an erect stem between two and three feet high. The cultivated varieties range widely in size, and in flower colour from white to dark purple.

There are about 200 species of *Aloe*, more than half of which come from South Africa. They usually have a basal rosette of stiff, lanceolate leaves, and are cultivated for their foliage. The **Partridge-breasted Aloe**, *A. variegata* [887], from Cape Province has triangular, erect leaves, arranged in three ranks, which are dark green with whitish bands; the hard edges and heel of the leaves are also white. The red, tubular flowers are borne in an erect, unbranched spike about 12 inches long. *A. aristata* [889], also from Cape Province, has a dense rosette, about eight inches across, of lanceolate, dark green leaves with white spiny margins. The long-stalked, reddish-yellow flowers are borne on an erect inflorescence about a foot high.

887

888

889

The genus *Allium* includes about 500 species of bulbous plants, with a more or less strong smell of onions, which are widely distributed in north temperate regions. Some are grown as vegetables and others as ornamental plants.

The **Chives**, *A. schoenoprasum* [890], occur throughout much of the north temperate zone and is found locally in England and Wales and North America in stony places. It has tufts of cylindrical, hollow leaves from four to 10 inches long. The erect stems are up to 15 inches long and bear dense terminal clusters of pale pink or purple flowers in June and July. The fruit is a capsule containing black, angular seeds.

890
891

454

A. victorialis [891] is a native of the Mediterranean region. It has clustered bulbs and oblong-lanceolate leaves from one to three inches wide. The spherical heads of white or yellowish stalked flowers are borne in May on the ends of erect stems from one to two feet high.

A. montanum [892] from Europe and northern Asia is a tufted perennial with linear, flat, greyish-green leaves. The erect stems, from eight to 20 inches high, terminate in semi-spherical heads of lilac-purple flowers which appear in July and August. A dwarf form, var. *petraeum*, is only six inches high.

A. karataviense [893] is an unusual species from Turkestan. It has large bulbs and two or three wide, bluish-green leaves. The central erect stem, about six inches high, bears a large, spherical, terminal head of white flowers in May. It is cultivated in rock-gardens.

892
893

455

894
895

456

Allium paradoxum [894] is a native of Persia and the Caucasus. It has narrow leaves up to a foot long. The erect stems, which are about as long as the leaves, bear from one to six long-stalked, nodding flowers. The perianth segments are white, the outer ones each having a green stripe. Small bulbils also occur with the flowers. These are organs of vegetative propagation and are easily detached. The genus *Erythronium* includes about 20 species widely distributed in the north temperate regions. The **Dog's-tooth Violet**, *E. dens-canis* [895], is a native of Europe and Asia. It has oval, pointed leaves about six inches long which are marked with brown and white patches. The solitary, drooping, pinkish-purple flowers, about two inches across, are borne on short, erect stems in March and April. The ovate perianth segments are markedly recurved. This species varies in habit and colour, and varieties with white to violet-purple flowers are in cultivation. Common American species have white or yellow flowers.

The genus *Fritillaria* includes about 80 species of north temperate bulbous plants with erect, unbranched stems and more or less nodding flowers. The magnificent **Crown Imperial**, *F. imperialis* [896, 899, coloured plate XXIIIa], is a native of the western Himalayas which was brought into cultivation about the end of the 16th century. It has a large, scaly bulb and a stout, erect stem from three to four feet high which bears on the lower part numerous lanceolate leaves up to six inches long. The ring of large, bell-shaped flowers is produced near the top of the stem beneath a terminal tuft of from eight to 20 small linear leaves. In the wild form the flowers

896

897

are about two inches long, and yellow or bronze in colour, but there are a number of cultivated forms with larger flowers of different colours. Among these are var. *maxima lutea* with large yellow flowers, and var. *maxima rubra* with large red flowers. With the exception of var. *inodora*, which has yellow or bronze flowers, the plant has a rather unpleasant foxy smell. The **Fritillary** or **Snake's Head**, *F. meleagris* [897], is a native of Europe and western Asia, and is found in damp pastures in a few scattered localities in England. It is frequently grown in gardens, and sometimes escapes. It has a small bulb about $\frac{1}{2}$ inch across and a slender erect stem from eight to 18 inches long.

Several glaucous, green, linear leaves from three to six inches long are borne about the middle of the stem. Usually a single terminal drooping flower is produced in April and May. The bell-shaped perianth is about an inch long with a chequered pattern of pale and dark purple. There is a conspicuous green nectary at the base of each perianth segment and the flowers are pollinated by bumble bees. The fruit is a globose capsule containing many flat seeds. The flowers vary in colour and there is a number of cultivated varieties. Var. *alba* has white flowers with green veins and var. *artemis* has grey-purple flowers. Several attractive species inhabit parts of western North America.

898

The genus *Lilium* includes about 90 species of north temperate plants which have bulbs with many overlapping fleshy scales. Many are valuable garden plants. Many species are native in the United States. The **Madonna Lily**, *L. candidum* [898], is a native of the eastern Mediterranean which has been cultivated

899

for many years. The basal leaves, which are produced during the autumn, and those borne on the lower part of the stem, are from six to eight inches long and up to an inch wide. The stems, between two and five feet high, bear from five to 20 large, pure white flowers during June. They are two or three inches long, trumpet-shaped with spreading segments. A large number of cultivated forms are known.

The **Martagon** or **Turk's Cap Lily**, *L. martagon* [900, 901], from Europe and Asia, has a bright yellow ovoid bulb and irregular whorls of lanceolate leaves. The stem, from two to four feet high, bears up to 50 flowers in June and July. They are over an inch across with recurved, purplish-red, spotted perianth segments.

The **Tiger Lily**, *L. tigrinum* [coloured plate XXI], is a native of China, Japan and Korea. It has linear, glossy green leaves and spotted, orange-red flowers from two to four inches long. It has run wild in the United States.

The genus *Tulipa* includes about 100 species native to Europe, western and central Asia and North Africa. They have bulbs with a thin papery covering which produce simple erect stems with few leaves and flowers. The flower has six similar, petaloid, perianth parts, six stamens and a three-celled ovary. The fruit is a capsule containing many flat seeds.

Tulipa tarda [902], which comes from Turkestan, has a rosette of from four to seven narrow, folded leaves about six inches long. The short stem bears from one to six flat, star-shaped flowers about two inches across during May. The ovate perianth parts are yellow at the base, white towards the tip, and marked with green and red lines on the outer surfaces.

Most of our garden **Tulips** have been derived from a plant named *T. gesneriana* [903, 904] which was introduced into Europe from Turkish gardens about the middle of the 16th century. Its origin is unknown and there is no known wild species which can be considered the ancestral form. On the other hand there is little doubt that some so-called species found in parts of Italy and France are forms of this plant which have become naturalized after escaping from cultivation. The main features of this plant are from three to four ovate, tapering leaves and a smooth

902

903

erect stem from 12 to 18 inches long. The flower is produced in April and May; owing to continued crossing and selection it is extremely variable in shape and colour. The position of the six stamens and central ovary with three stigmas can be well seen in the X-ray photograph of a mature flower [904].

904

The distortion and mottling of the petals seen in the **Parrot Tulips** [905] is caused by the presence of a virus.

Scilla bifolia [906] is a native of the Mediterranean region. It usually has two narrow leaves from four to eight inches long. The erect stems bear from three to eight blue, white or reddish flowers during March. The flowers are small and have spreading perianth segments.

905
906

The genus *Eucomis* includes about 10 species of bulbous plants from tropical and South Africa. *E. regia* [907] has a globose bulb and from six to eight leaves up to 18 inches wide and four inches across. The stout central stem bears a dense mass of green flowers and above this a terminal crown of between 12 and 20 leaves.

The genus *Ornithogalum* embraces about 100 species which occur in Europe, western Asia and Africa. They are small, bulbous plants with linear leaves marked by a medium white stripe. *O. gussonei* [908] grows in grassy places in central and southern Europe and the Caucasus. It is up to a foot high and its small groups of pure white flowers appear in April and May. *O. fimbriatum* [909] is a native of Asia Minor. It has hairy, linear leaves from six to eight inches long and the clusters of from eight to 20 greenish-white flowers appear in February. *O. umbellatum* is now wild in the United States, having escaped from cultivation.

The 40 species belonging to the genus *Muscari* occur in Europe, western Asia and North Africa. In the southern United States *M. racemosum* has escaped from cultivation to such an extent as to become a troublesome weed.

908
909

465

910

911

Grape Hyacinth, *M. atlanticum* [910], is a native of central and southern Europe and southern Russia. It also grows on dry grassland in a few localities in England. Each small bulb produces from three to five linear grooved leaves up to a foot long. The stalked dense group of small, dark blue globular flowers appears in April and May.

The **Tassel Hyacinth,** *M. comosum* [911], has a similar range to that of the **Grape Hyacinth** but occurs only as a garden escape in Britain. It has broader leaves and the loose erect spike of flowers up to 20 inches high appears between April and July. The flowers are of two types: spreading, brown, fertile flowers, and purple erect ones which are sterile.

M. lingulatum [912] is a native of Asia
Minor. Each bulb produces a few smooth,
somewhat fleshy, tongue-shaped leaves
from two to three inches long. The dense
inflorescence which appears in the spring
consists of from 20 to 30 small blue
flowers borne on a central erect stem
about three inches long.

The **Striped Squill**, *Puschkinia scilloides*
[913], is a native of Asia Minor, the
Caucasus and Afghanistan. The few
more or less erect leaves are dark green,
lanceolate and from four to six inches
long. The erect stem is from four to eight
inches long and bears a loose terminal
cluster of several flowers in April or May.
The flower is up to one inch across with
spreading perianth segments which are
blue with white stripes.

467

914

915

Most of our garden **Hyacinths** are derived from *Hyacinthus orientalis* [914], a native of eastern Mediterranean and western Asia. It has a large bulb with a purple or white scaly covering and from four to six linear-lanceolate, hooded, bright green leaves. The flowers are produced in spring on a terminal cylindrical cluster on a central stem from six to 12 inches high. The wild form has from five to 15 flowers but cultivated varieties have many more. The fragrant, more or less nodding, funnel-shaped flowers are about an inch long with recurved perianth segments. Most cultivated varieties are white or various shades of red and blue.

468

916

Veltheimia viridiflora [915] is a South African plant with wavy, intense green leaves from eight to 12 inches long. The crowded heads of tubular, reddish or yellowish, spotted flowers are borne during April on erect, unbranched stems from one to 1½ feet long.

Silkgrass or **Spoonleaf Yucca**, *Yucca filamentosa* [916], is an evergreen from the south-east United States. It has a basal rosette of somewhat glaucous, lanceolate leaves up to about two feet long. The large,

erect inflorescence, from three to six feet high, bears a large number of yellowish-white pendulous flowers. Many other yuccas are native to south-western North America.

The **Aspidistra**, *Aspidistra lurida* [coloured plate XXIIIb], is a native of China which has long been used as a house plant. It has sombre green leaves up to 20 inches long and produces solitary purplish flowers at soil level.

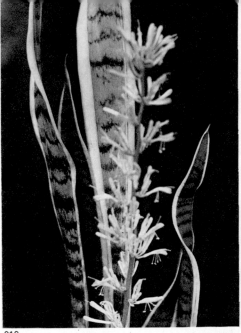

918

919

The genus *Dracaena* includes about 40 species which are among the few members of the family that reach tree-like dimensions. The **Dragon Tree**, *D. draco* [917], is a native of the Canary Islands. It is densely branched, woody, from 30 to 60 feet high, and has crowded, sword-shaped leaves up to two feet long. *D. fragrans* [920] from Guinea is used for internal decoration. It has large glossy leaves up to three feet long, spherical clusters of yellow flowers and orange-red berries. *Sansevieria trifasciata* [918] from tropical Africa, commonly grown indoors, has a creeping rhizome and erect, stiff leaves from one to four feet high. The greenish flowers are borne in an erect inflorescence from one to two feet high. *Ruscus hypoglossum* [919], which is found in southern Europe, is a small evergreen shrub with stiff, spiny, flattened green stems and leaves reduced to small scales.

920

921

Lily-of-the-Valley, *Convallaria majalis* [921], occurs in Europe and western Asia and is also found in woods on non-acid soils in England. It is often cultivated and is frequently found as an escape in Europe and North America. It has a branched rhizome and short, erect stems each having several papery scales at the base and two dark green leaves up to six inches long. In May or June each erect stem bears from six to 12 white, fragrant, bell-shaped flowers about ½ inch across. The fruit is a red berry. *C. montana* of the south-eastern United States is believed to be native there.

XXIXa *Cymbidium cultum*

XXIXb *Paphiopedilum cultum*

XXX   *Phragmopedilum hybridum*

The family *Trilliaceae* is a small family of about 25 species of north temperate plants which were formerly included in the family *Liliaceae*. They are rhizomatous herbs with opposite leaves. The perianth usually consists of two different whorls.

Herb Paris, *Paris quadrifolia* [922], occurs throughout Europe and western Asia and has a scattered distribution in damp woods on calcareous soils in Britain. The slender creeping rhizome gives rise to erect, unbranched stems up to 15 inches high with four spreading, ovate, pointed leaves from two to four inches long at the top. The terminal flower appears between May and July. It has four pointed green sepals, four narrow yellow petals, eight stamens and a central ovary with four styles. The flower, not being brightly coloured, does not attract bees, butterflies, etc., but its foetid smell attracts small flies. As the stigmas are receptive before the pollen is released cross-pollination is effected. The blackish, fleshy, spherical fruit looks like a berry but it eventually releases the seeds.

Wake Robin, *Trillium grandiflorum* [923], is a native of eastern North America. The solitary stem, from 12 to 18 inches high, bears three ovate, pointed leaves from three to five inches long. The solitary terminal flower, which appears between April and June, has three narrow sepals and three ovate, white or pink petals.

922

923

924

925

The family *Amaryllidaceae* [924–935, coloured plate XXII] includes about 500 species which have a wide distribution but are particularly common in warm temperate regions. They are perennial herbs with basal leaves and underground bulbs, rhizomes or corms. The bisexual flowers have a petaloid perianth of two whorls of three parts and six stamens which may be free or attached to the perianth. The three-celled ovary is inferior. Usually the fruit is a capsule, rarely a berry. Economically the family is mainly important for the large number of species with attractive flowers which are widely grown in gardens.

The familiar **Snowdrop**, *Galanthus nivalis* [924], is widespread in damp woods in England and Wales, central and southern Europe, and western Asia. It is often planted and has become naturalized elsewhere. It has an underground bulb and linear leaves from four to 10 inches long. The solitary, nodding flowers, subtended by a greenish spathe, are produced on erect, unbranched stems between January and March. The completely white outer perianth parts are spreading and the inner ones are erect and marked with a green blotch. The fruit is an ovoid capsule.

The **Spring Snowflake**, *Leucojum vernum* [925], occurs in scattered localities on hills in central and southern Europe and is found very rarely in south-west England. It has a large bulb and bright green leaves up to a foot long. The nodding, bell-shaped flowers are usually borne singly on erect stems between February and April. The ovate perianth parts are white, tipped with green. The pear-shaped capsule contains pale seeds.

9

927

928

The genus *Haemanthus* includes about 60 species from southern and tropical Africa. They have large bulbs and usually broad, curved leaves. The flowers are borne in a single spherical head up to a foot across which terminates the thick erect stem. Forms sometimes cultivated include *H. coccineus* [926], *H. katherinae* [927], both with red flowers, as well as many hybrids [coloured plate XXII].

The genus *Hippeastrum* includes about 70 species of bulbous plants from tropical America. One of the most commonly grown is *H. vittatum* [928] which has from six to eight leaves about two feet long, and a longer erect stem bearing from three to six reddish-white flowers each about five inches across.

Clivia miniata [929] from Natal has long, sword-shaped leaves and spherical heads of large showy red and yellow flowers.

The **Amazon Lily**, *Eucharis grandiflora* [930], from Colombia has a spherical bulb and leaves about two feet long. The erect stem, up to two feet long, bears from three to six starshaped flowers about four inches across. Of interest is the ring formed by the flattened filaments of the stamens which indicates how the corona of daffodils may have evolved. *Hymenocallis caribaea* [931], one of the **Spider Lilies**, is a native of the West Indies. It has a globose bulb and leaves from two to three feet long. Between six and 12 flowers are produced at the top of the long stem. Each has narrow, curved perianth segments and a central toothed cup about an inch deep. Several other species occur in the southeastern United States.

930

931

There are about 35 wild species of *Narcissus* and a bewildering variety of cultivated forms. The **Pheasant Eye**, *N. poeticus* [932], which has been divided into several separate species, comes from the Mediterranean region; many varieties are known. It has fragrant white flowers which have a short, wavy, red-margined corona. The **Tazetta Narcissus**, *N. tazetta* [934], is widespread from the Canary Isles to Japan. It is about 18 inches high and has from four to 12 pale yellow flowers each 1½ inches across.

The **Wild Daffodil**, *N. pseudonarcissus* [933], occurs in damp woods in England, Wales and western Europe. The bulb produces several narrow leaves and solitary yellow flowers with long trumpets between February and April.

932

933

934

935

936

Most of the 300 species of *Agave* occur in Mexico. Several are cultivated as **Maguey** and **Mescal**, being used for the production of alcoholic beverages. *A. filifera* [935] has a dense rosette of stiff, spiny leaves about two feet long and an inflorescence of maroon flowers which is from 10 to 15 feet high. Sisal is obtained from the leaves of *A. sisalana*. *Tacca macrantha* [936] from tropical south-eastern Asia belongs to the family *Taccaceae*. The group of drooping flowers is subtended by a large coloured bract and several filamentous bracteoles.

The **Iris** family, *Iridaceae* [937–950, coloured plates XXIV, XXV], includes well over 1,000 species widely distributed throughout the world. They are perennial herbs with underground rhizomes, corms or bulbs. The leaves are long and narrow with sheathing bases and do not have stalks. The bisexual flowers have a petaloid perianth of six parts in two whorls which are fused at the base to form a tube. There are three stamens and the three-celled ovary is inferior. The fruit is a capsule opening by valves. The family is mainly important for the large number of plants with showy flowers which are extensively cultivated.

There are about 80 species of *Crocus*, mainly centred in the Mediterranean region. Many forms of *C. aureus* and *C. vernus*, together with about a dozen species, are cultivated. *C. heuffelianus* [937] is a Hungarian species which flowers in March. It produces three linear leaves about five inches long and purplish flowers. A distinct variety with rose-purple flowers and a yellow throat is found in the Carpathians. *C. chrysanthus* [coloured plate XXV] is a native of Greece and Asia Minor. It produces from five to seven narrow leaves and bright orange flowers in February.

The 200 species of *Iris* are north temperate plants with rhizomes or bulbs. They vary greatly in size and in form and colour of the flower, and there are many hundreds of cultivated varieties. *I. reichenbachii* [938] from the Balkans has stems from six to 10 inches high and leaves from three to six inches long. The flowers, which appear in April, are either brown-and-white or yellow-and-orange, but one distinct variety from the Bulgarian mountains [942] has purple flowers.

937
938

481

Iris reticulata [939] is a small species from the Caucasus that flowers in February and March. From two to four leaves eventually reach a foot in length but are much shorter at the time of flowering. The flowers are deep purple with narrow perianth segments, the inner ones having an orange ridge. It is commonly grown in rock-gardens.

939
940

Iris persica [940], a native of Asia Minor and southern Persia, is another small species. It has a tuft of from four to five curved leaves about three inches long and a stem which bears one, or rarely two, flowers in February. The flowers have a violet scent and are greenish-blue with the outer perianth parts having bright yellow keels. The flowers of cultivated varieties range from creamy-white to dark purple.

Iris graminea [941] is found in central and southern Europe. It has a compressed stem up to nine inches high and about four basal leaves which project above the flowers. The deep purple flowers appear in May and June. They are about two inches long and have a smell of ripe plums.

Iris hybrida [943] embraces a group of modern tall varieties known only in cultivation. Their origin is obscure. The fruits of Iris spp. [944] are erect, elongated, three-sided capsules. The wall breaks open from the top as valves, exposing the numerous large seeds.

941

943

942

944

The **Japanese Iris**, *Iris kaempferi* [945], is an attractive species up to two feet high. Each erect stem usually bears two flowers in July, about three inches long; in the wild type they are reddish-purple, but the cultivated varieties have a great range of colour and pattern.

Iris aphylla [946] from eastern Europe and the Caucasus has curved, glaucous green leaves which die down completely during the winter. The forked stems bearing the flowers are about a foot long. Flowering occurs in the spring but more flowers may be produced in the autumn. The flower is dark lilac and over two inches long.

The **Flower of Tigris** or **Peacock Tiger Flower**, *Tigridia pavonia* [948], is a native of Mexico. The spear-shaped leaves are from 12 to 18 inches long and the flowers, mostly in groups of three, are borne on stems from one to two feet high in June. Each flower is about three inches across and the three stigmas are small, unlike the large petaloid ones of the Iris. The flowers of the wild form are orange, but in cultivation they range from white to purple.

There are about 120 species in the genus *Gladiolus*. They differ from *Iris* spp. in having underground corms. The perianth segments are all similar and often narrow and the perianth tube is bent. *G. imbricatus*

946

947
948

[947] is a native of eastern Europe and southern
Russia. It is from one to two feet high and two or
three leaves are produced by each corm. Between four
and 10 flowers are borne on the erect one-sided spikes
in June and July. The perianth tube is sharply bent
and the dark purple segments are more or less equal
in size and shape and narrowed at the base. *G. gandavensis* [949, coloured plate XXIV] is the general
name embracing many of the colourful garden
gladioli. It appears to have arisen as a hybrid between
two South African species, *G. psittacinus* and *G. car-
dinalis*. Crossing with other species has produced
many variations from the original crimson flower.

485

949

951

950

The genus *Freesia* includes four South African species with underground corms. *F. refracta* [950] is about 18 inches high with five or six linear leaves and greenish-yellow flowers. A variety of this species. var. *leicht-linii*, with yellow flowers larger than normal, was crossed with the pink-flowered *F. armstrongii* in 1898. As a result the hybrid *F.* × *kewensis* was introduced from which all our colourful, fragrant forms derived.

The **Rush** family, *Juncaceae* [951–953], includes about 350 herbaceous perennials found mostly in temperate regions. They are rhizomatous, often tufted, and have long narrow leaves. The small, bisexual, wind-pollinated flowers are often crowded into more or less dense clusters. Each has six green or brown perianth parts in two whorls, six stamens and a small central ovary with a feathery, branched stigma. The fruit is a capsule.

Over 200 species belong to the genus *Juncus*. They vary in size and habit but always have numerous seeds in the capsules. *J. conglomeratus* [951] is widespread in wet places throughout the British Isles, Europe, North Africa and Newfoundland. It is densely tufted with dull green ridged stems from one to five feet long. The lateral dense brown clusters of flowers are produced between May and July. The **Soft Rush**, *J. effusus*, is similar but has smooth stems and lax clusters of flowers which are produced earlier.

The genus *Luzula* includes about 80 species of grass-like hairy perennials with only three seeds in the fruit. The **Hairy Woodrush**, *L. pilosa* [953], occurs in shady places in the British Isles, Europe and north-west Asia. It is about a foot high and flowers during May. The **Sedge** family, *Cyperaceae* [953–960], has a world-wide distribution and includes at least 3,000

952

953

species. They usually grow in wet places, and are mostly rhizomatous perennials with narrow leaves and small, bisexual, wind-pollinated flowers. Each flower is in the axil of a small bract and the perianth consists of a few bristles or is absent. Frequently the flowers are crowded together in spikelets. The fruit is a smal, one-seeded, indehiscent nut.

Cladium mariscus [953] occurs widely in non-acid fens in warm temperate regions. In the British Isles it is most frequent in East Anglia and western Ireland. It is a stout perennial from two to 10 feet high with long, sharp leaves. The terminal branched inflorescence bears heads of few-flowered spikelets in July and August. The flowers are usually bisexual and the ovoid fruit is dark brown. A similar species, *C. mariscoides*, is found in North America.

Two **Cotton-grasses**, *Eriophorum angustifolium* [954] and *E. vaginatum* [957], are widespread in arctic and north temperate regions, particularly in bogs. They are both rhizomatous perennials, the former far-creeping and the latter tufted, with narrow, pointed, grass-like leaves. Flowering occurs between April and June, the small bisexual flowers being arranged in spikelets. In *E. angustifolium* there are usually several nodding spikelets on each stem; in *E. vaginatum* there is a single erect spikelet. The fruits bear conspicuous, white, cottony hairs.

954
955

XXXI *Ananas comosus* (**Pineapple**)

XXXII *Hedychium gardnerianum*

956

Cyperus alternifolius [955] is a perennial from Madagascar. It has stiff erect stems from one to 2½ feet long with a group of crowded leaves near the top. Above this a large number of stalked clusters of spikelets may be produced. The **Egyptian Paper Reed**, *C. papyrus* [956], is a perennial with dark green stems up to 10 feet long bearing terminal tufts of leaves. The ancient Egyptians used dried strips to make papyrus.

957

958

959

960

Scirpus maritimus [958] is a rhizomatous perennial which grows in the mud of rivers near the sea. It reaches a height of three feet and the stalked, terminal clusters of reddish-brown, ovoid spikelets appear in July and August.

The world-wide genus *Carex* includes at least 1,000 species. These are the true sedges. Among them is *C. acuta* [959], which grows in wet places. It is a tufted perennial with erect leaves and stems. There are from one to three upper spikes of male flowers and from two to four lower spikes of female flowers. *C. flava* [960] is widespread in North America and elsewhere, but rare in Britain. It is seldom more than two feet high and has a single male spike and from two to four female spikes.

961

The **Orchid** family, *Orchidaceae* [961-991, coloured plates XXVI-XXX], includes about 800 genera and probably 20,000 species and is perhaps the largest family of flowering plants. Although mainly tropical in distribution, representatives are found throughout the world. They are all perennial herbs with rhizomes or tuberous roots and many have swollen stem bases or pseudo-bulbs. Some are terrestrial but many tropical and subtropical species are epiphytic. These grow on tree branches or trunks and generally have aerial roots which hang freely down. The simple, entire leaves are often thick and leathery and arranged spirally or in two opposite rows. Some species have no leaves.

The flowers may be solitary or borne in inflorescences of various kinds. In spite of the vast range of size, form and colour of the flowers, often with bizarre effects, there is a basic uniformity in floral plan throughout the family. The outer perianth whorl consists of three sepals which are usually similar and either resemble other sepals or are petaloid. The three inner segments are often larger and the posterior one is usually different from the others. This petal, the labellum, is often lobed and comes to lie on the lower side of the flower owing to the twisting of the flower stalk through 180° during development or to the inversion of the whole flower in a pendulous inflorescence. In the centre is a variously shaped structure, the column, which consists of style, stigma or stigmas, and stamens. In one group of orchids there are three stigmas (or a three-lobed stigma) and two stamens, but in the majority only two receptive stigmas are found and there is only one stamen. The anthers are borne on the tip of the column and contain one or a few masses of pollen grains (pollinia). Many extraordinary insect-pollinating mechanisms are found in the orchids. In many the pollinia become attached to the bodies of insect visitors and then come into contact with the stigmas of other flowers.

The one-celled ovary is inferior. After pollination it gives rise to an elongated capsule containing an enormous number of minute seeds. These contain little food material and undifferentiated embryos and are easily wind-dispersed. Contact with a fungus is necessary for germination (except in experimental culture) and subsequent growth is very slow. This fungal association is retained in the older plant but its significance is a matter of debate. Most orchids are green and can synthesize their own food material. The few non-green saprophytes have scale leaves and are dependent upon the fungus for organic food.

The **Lady's Slipper** or **Moccasin-flower**, *Cypripedium calceolus* [961, 962], occurs mainly in woods on alkaline soils in Europe, northern Asia and North America. It is also a native in England but is very rare. It is a rhizomatous perennial from six to 18 inches high. The three or four sheathing leaves at the base of each stem are ovate-oblong and conspicuously ribbed. There is usually only a single flower at the end of the erect stem with a leaf-like bract some distance below it. The beautiful flower, which appears in May or June, is about three inches across. The three outer sepals are maroon, the upper one ovate and the two lateral ones more or less fused together forming a bifid segment behind the labellum. The two lateral inner petals are narrow and somewhat twisted. The pale yellow labellum projects forwards and has the form of a short slipper with a rounded tip. It is marked with dark lines on the outside and red spots inside. The labellum's smooth wall and incurved rim prevents intruding insects from getting out other than by crawling past the column. Here they come in contact with the stigma and anthers and effect cross-pollination. This is one of the orchids with two stamens and the pollen grains are not in compact masses.

The Old World genus *Paphio-pedilum* is closely related to *Cypripedium* and is included in that genus by some experts. It has often been used by orchid breeders and many beautiful hybrids, such as *P. cultum* [coloured plate XXIXb], have been produced.

The **Fly Orchid**, *Ophrys insecti-fera* [963, 965], occurs in Europe and the British Isles, particularly in woods and scrub on calcareous soils. It has ovoid root tubers, a few oblong leaves, and smooth, erect stems from one to two feet high. Between four and 12 flowers are borne towards the end of the erect stem between May and July. The three spreading sepals are yellowish-green. The two lateral perianth segments are short purplish-brown projecting structures. The large, lobed, velvety labellum is purplish-brown with a conspicuous bluish central patch. The whole flower resembles an insect and presumably attracts insect visitors which are essential for the production of viable seeds.

962
963

493

964

Phragmopedilum grande [964] is a hybrid between the tropical American species *P. caudatum* and *P. longifolium*. It has long, dark green leaves and an erect stem up to three feet high with several shiny, yellowish-green flowers. The two lateral petals are very long and twisted and the labellum is deeply concave. Other very beautiful cultivated hybrids are grown [coloured plate XXX].

966

967

One of the most common and also one of the most difficult genera of European terrestrial orchids is *Orchis*. There is considerable variation in form, and hybridization is common. The spotted and marsh orchids have lobed root tubers and are often put into a separate genus. *Dactylorchis*. However, even when thus restricted the group remains variable and

identification is often difficult. The **Common Spotted Orchid**, *D. fuchsii* [966], occurs widely in wet non-acid soils. It usually has spotted leaves but sometimes they are uniformly green. The flowers range from white to reddish-purple and the erect spikes are from $\frac{1}{2}$ to six inches long. Five of the perianth parts are more or less spreading and the lobed, variegated

968

labellum has a downwardly projecting spur. *D. sambucina* [967] is a European species which grows in dry, non-calcareous meadows. It is a foot or more in height and has bright green leaves. The spikes of yellow or reddish-violet flowers are produced in April and May. The **Green-winged Orchid**, *Orchis morio* [968], is widespread in Europe, western Asia and Asia Minor. In Britain it is sometimes common in calcareous grassland. It has rounded tubers and broadly lanceolate leaves. The flowery spikes are from five to 15 inches high and may appear early before the snow cover has melted. The five perianth segments of the reddish-purple flowers form a hood over the columns. The three-lobed labellum has a long, straight spur.

969

970

The **Lady Orchid**, *Orchis purpurea* [969], occurs in Europe, the Caucasus and Asia Minor, and is a rare species in chalk scrub of the extreme south-east part of England. It has an ovoid tuber and smooth, shiny, broadly lanceolate leaves. The erect spikes of handsome, dark reddish-purple flowers are from one to two feet high and appear in May. The lobed labellum has a notched spur.

The **Soldier Orchid**, *Orchis militaris* [970], is wide-spread in Europe and western Asia and is another rare plant of chalk grassland in southern England. It has a globose tuber and smooth, elliptical leaves. The stout stem, from eight to 18 inches high, terminates in a short, dense flowering spike which appears in May or June. The hood is greyish and flushed with red. The lobed labellum is whitish centrally but is marked with violet spots and has a violet margin. The cylindrical spur curves downward and forward.

971

The Long-leaved Helleborine, *Cephalanthera longifolia* [972], occurs widely in Europe and Asia and is found in scattered localities in Britain, particularly in the shade on calcareous soils. It has a creeping rhizome, lanceolate, folded leaves and erect flowering spikes up to two feet long. The distant, pure white flowers appear between May and July. They never open widely, but appear to be pollinated by bees.

972

Himantoglossum hircinum [971], the **Lizard Orchid**, occurs in scattered localities in southern and eastern England. It is also found in central Europe and the Mediterranean region. It has ovoid root tubers and elliptical leaves. The long spikes of greenish-purple flowers smell strongly of goats; they appear between May and July. The labellum has two lateral twisted lobes and a short conical spur.

973

974

The **Ghost Orchid**, *Epipogium aphyllum* [973], occurs from northern Europe to the Himalayas and has been found a few times in Britain. It is a rhizomatous, non-green saprophyte which grows in deep woodland shade. The translucent stem is from four to eight inches long and bears a few yellowish flowers.

Listera cordata [974], the **Lesser Twayblade**, occurs in mountain woods in the British Isles, Europe, Asia and North America. It has slender creeping rhizomes and erect stems from three to eight inches high. Near the base are two ovate leaves, and at the top is a loose cylindrical spike of tiny reddish-green flowers.

975

The genus *Coelogyne* includes about 120 species of small epiphytic orchids which vary greatly in habit. *C. cristata* [975] from the Himalayas is about 18 inches high. It has smooth ovoid pseudo-bulbs and long, leathery, bright green leaves about two inches wide. The beautiful, white, fragrant flowers are borne in drooping spikes. This is one of the most popular orchids in cultivation and one of the easiest to grow.

976

977

The genus *Dendrochilum*, which consists of about 100 species, is widely distributed in East Borneo, Java and the Philippines. The flowers are generally small and are borne in a dense, stalked inflorescence. *D. glumaceum* [976] comes from the Philippines. It has broad leaves and a pointed spike of white or creamy-white flowers which is borne on a slender, curved stalk.

Epidendrum is a large genus of orchids which are mostly epiphytic. The majority are natives of the West Indies and Brazil but some occur in Florida. Great variation in habit is found, and pseudo-bulbs are often present. The flowers, too, vary greatly and may be produced singly or in clusters. They are often dull-coloured but some species with bright flowers also occur. *Epidendrum falcatum* [977] from Mexico has a stout rhizome, thick pseudo-bulbs and fleshy, tapering leaves from six to 12 inches long. The creamy-white flowers are four inches or more across, and each has five narrow, spreading perianth segments. The labellum projects forwards and has two lateral lobes and a narrow, pointed central lobe. The exclusively Old World genus *Dendrobium* includes about 900 species from India, Burma, Malaya, China, Japan and the Philippines. They vary greatly in habit from moss-like forms to some which are among the largest orchids known. Pseudo-bulbs are generally well developed. The flowers are generally fragrant but a few have an unattractive scent. The perianth segments are more or less equal. Each flower produces four pollen masses. *D. nobile* [978, coloured plate XXVIIb] is a native of north India, Assam and China. This is one of the best-known species in cultivation and one of the easiest to grow. It has stout, fleshy

pseudo-bulbs from two to three feet high, with from six to 10 bright green leaves. The fragrant flowers are produced freely at the nodes of two-year-old pseudo-bulbs, and in greenhouses generally appear between January and April. There are many named varieties varying in flower colour from white to deep purple.

979
980

The genus *Cattleya* includes about 40 species and a number of natural hybrids, all epiphytic orchids from Mexico, central America, Brazil or Peru. They have forked pseudo-bulbs, each with a single oval leaf. The flowers are magnificent and may reach up to 10 inches across. *C. labiata* [979, coloured plate XXVIa] from Brazil has pseudo-bulbs up to a foot high and dark green, leathery leaves up to 10 inches long. Each stem bears from three to seven flowers which are from six to seven inches across. The five spreading perianth segments are broad, the two lateral petals being waved. The labellum is somewhat hooded and in the wild form is deep velvety-crimson. This beautiful orchid is extremely variable and the flowers range in colour from white with yellow markings to deep purple. It is frequently used for hybridization both with other *Cattleya* spp. [coloured plate XXVIb] and with closely related genera, e.g. *Brassavola*. producing *Brassocattleya* [coloured plate XXVIIa].

Dendrobium phalaenopsis var. *schroederianum* [980] from New Guinea has pseudo-bulbs from two to three feet long. Up to 20 large flowers are borne in each pendulous cluster. The lateral petals are larger than the sepals and the tubular labellum has a projecting lower lip. The flowers range in colour from white to purple.

The genus *Catasetum* includes about 100 species of orchids from the West Indies, tropical America and Brazil. They have obconical pseudobulbs which are often folded and ribbed, and broadly lanceolate leaves. The flowers are unisexual and the male and female flowers, which are borne on separate spikes usually on different plants, may differ in structure. Generally there are fewer female flowers and they are unknown in a number of species. *C. maculatum* [981] is a native of Mexico, Guatemala and Venezuela. The greyish flowers are purple spotted and have a large inflated labellum, In the male flower the column has two horn-like projections which lie across the mouth of the labellum. These are sensitive and, when touched, the pollen masses are ejected with considerable force.

981

982

505

983

984

Stanhopea is a genus of about 50 species of epiphytic orchids from tropical America and Brazil. The inflorescence bears between two and seven stalked flowers which are large and strongly scented; usually they do not last long. The oblong spreading perianth parts are broad at the base. The labellum is thick and fleshy and often has a very complex structure. *S. tigrina* [982–985] is a native of Mexico with large, broadly lanceolate, dark green, folded leaves. The orange-yellow flowers, which appear in July and September, are up to eight inches across. The perianth parts are spreading but the large spotted labellum has a remarkable resemblance to a skull. This is seen particularly well in face view [984] and its complex structure can be well appreciated from X-ray photographs taken from the side [983] and the front [985]. This is the finest and best-known member of the genus. Several varieties are known, including those with deep yellow and brownish-purple flowers.

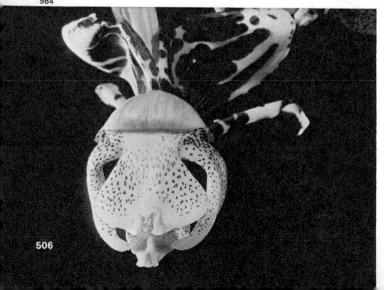

986

Macroplectrum sesquipedale [988] is a native of Madagascar. It has two opposite rows of leaves which are broadly lanceolate and up to 12 inches long. The flowering stem bears several flowers from five to seven inches across, white or creamy-white; each has a long, thin, curved spur up to 11 inches long. Charles Darwin predicted that a moth with a proboscis as long as the spur would be found on the island and he was proved correct some years later.

Cymbidium insigne [989] is a beautiful, variable species from Assam. It has narrow, glaucous leaves from 20 to 30 inches long, globose pseudo-bulbs, and flowering spikes from three to four feet high. The flowers are pinkish-red with darker spots. There are many cultivated species and hybrids of *Cymbidium* [coloured plate XXIXa].

987

The genus *Oncidium* includes about 500 species of epiphytic orchids from the West Indies, Peru and Ecuador, where they often grow at considerable elevations; and a few occur in Florida. *O. cavendishianum* [986] from Guatemala has broad, leathery leaves from seven to 15 inches long, and no pseudo-bulbs. The inflorescence, from two to three feet high, bears a number of fragrant flowers about 1½ inches across. The undulate perianth parts are yellowish-green with red spots and the lobed labellum is bright yellow. *O. varicosum* [987] from Brazil has conical, ribbed pseudo-bulbs and broadly lanceolate leaves from six to nine inches long. It grows vigorously, and the inflorescence bears between 80 and 90 yellowish-green and brown flowers. The large, lobed labellum is bright yellow.

988
990

989

Odontoglossum grande [990] from Guatemala has oblong, dark green leaves from six to nine inches long, and from four to seven orange-yellow, banded flowers on each erect stem. There are also cultivated forms with different-coloured flowers [coloured plate XXVIII].

Vanda tricolor [991] from Java has leathery leaves and sprays of fragrant, pale-yellow flowers with brown spots. There are many cultivated varieties of this beautiful orchid.

The **Bur-reed** family, *Sparganiaceae*, includes about
15 species of perennial aquatic herbs which are
widespread, but not found in South America or
Africa. *S. erectum* [992, 993] is a variable species
which occurs throughout the north temperate regions
including the British Isles. It grows in shallow water
and has erect leaves up to five feet long. The branched
inflorescence, which appears between June and
August, has spherical heads of unisexual flowers, the
smaller male heads towards the top and the fewer and
larger female heads towards the base of each branch.
The flowers are wind-pollinated and the one-seeded
fruits are indehiscent.

994

995

The **Reedmace** or **Cat-tail** family, sometimes wrongly called *Typhaceae*, consists of the single genus *Typha* with about nine species distributed throughout the world. The **Great Reedmace** or **Cat's-tail**, *T. latifolia* [994], is found over most of the range of the genus except in Australia, southern Asia and central and South Africa. It occurs in reedswamps in the shallow margins of ponds, rivers and canals, and is often found in large, dense stands. It is a stout perennial with a thick rhizome growing in the mud and erect linear leaves up to eight feet long. The minute unisexual flowers are borne in dense inflorescences on stout stems during June and July. Each

flower has a ring of hairs or scales which are described as the perianth. The male inflorescence is terminal; each flower has from two to five stamens. After the pollen is shed the flowers wither and leave a bare length of stem above the fruiting region. The cylindrical female inflorescence occurs just beneath the male inflorescence. The dark brown fruiting mass remains unchanged for some time but eventually it breaks up and the seeds are released [995].

The **Lesser Reedmace**, *T. angustifolia*, is a similar plant but not so large; usually there is a distinct gap between the male and female inflorescences. The spikes are often used for decoration.

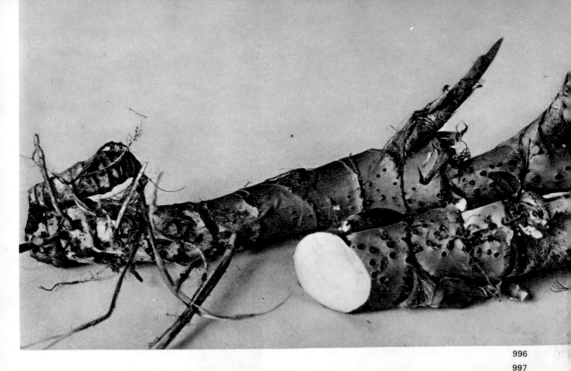

The **Arum** family, *Araceae*
[996–1009], includes about
1,500 species, most of which
are tropical or subtropical
in distribution. Most are
terrestrial, rhizomatous
perennials, but some are
climbers and a few are
aquatic. The small flowers
are bisexual or unisexual
and crowded on a fleshy
receptacle or spadix which is
more or less enclosed in a
sheath-like spathe. The perianth is usually absent in unisexual flowers. The fleshy or
hard fruit may contain one
or many seeds. The family
is not of great economic
importance except for **Taro**,
Colocasia esculenta, an important staple article of diet
throughout the Pacific, and
is widely cultivated. A
number of species are
grown for ornament.

513

998
1000

999

The **Sweet Flag**, *Acorus calamus* [996, 997], is a native of southern Asia and central and western North America. It was introduced into Europe about the middle of the 16th century and had become established in England by 1660. It grows in shallow water on the edges of ponds and streams. The thick perennial rhizome [996] grows in the mud, and the long, narrow leaves project into the air. The leaves, which are up to three feet long, are slightly curved; they have a very characteristic smell when crushed. The cylindrical, tapered spadix, up to three inches long, appears between May and July. It appears to be lateral because the pointed spathe seems to be a continuation of the compressed stem. The small, crowded, yellowish flowers are bisexual, but in Britain at least fertile fruits have not been found. The sweet-scented leaves of this plant were formerly used for covering floors.

The genus *Anthurium* [998–1000] includes about 600 species of tropical herbs and climbers. *A. crystallinum* [998] is a native of Peru which is sometimes grown for

1001

its beautiful heart-shaped, velvety leaves which are dark green with conspicuous white veins. *A. splendidum* [999] from Colombia has glaucous green leaves with brown veins. There are many varieties; the spathe is often bright red. *A. andraeanum* [1000], also a native of Colombia, has drooping lanceolate leaves. The wrinkled, heart-shaped spathe is from six to 10 inches long, orange-red in colour, and the erect spadix is yellowish. There are also a number of varieties with different colours in cultivation.

Lysichitum camtschatcense [1001] occurs in swamps in eastern Siberia and Japan. The oblong leaves are up to four feet long and one foot across. The spadix, bearing many bisexual flowers and enclosed by a hooded white spathe, appears in June. The fruits consist of two-seeded berries embedded in the spadix. Another species, *L. americanum*, from Alaska, Oregon and California, has yellow spathes. It is locally called **Skunk-cabbage**.

Calla palustris [1002] grows in swamps and wet woods in central and northern Europe, and in northern regions of Asia and America. It has also become naturalized in England. It is a perennial from six to 12 inches high with a creeping rhizome and stalked leaves which have smooth, entire, heart-shaped blades. The short, stout spadix, which appears in June and July, is completely covered with flowers and is subtended by a flat, oval, white or yellowish spathe. The fruit is a red berry.

The genus *Amorphophallus* includes about 60 species of large tuberous plants from tropical regions of the Old World, Australia and the Pacific. They usually have compound leaves, unisexual flowers and a cup- or bell-shaped spathe at the base of the spadix. *A. bulbifer* [1003] has dull green, variegated, dissected leaves up to four feet long. The pinkish spadix is about three inches long, and the green spathe is reddish at the base outside and yellow at the top inside. Some species are much larger; for example *A. titanum* from Sumatra has leaves 15 feet across.

The genus *Dieffenbachia* includes about 12 species of tropical American perennials. *D. picta* [1004] is a native of Brazil with a thick, erect stem and dark green, oblong leaves marked with white and pale green blotches. This is a variable species, and forms with different types of leaf markings are known.

There are about eight species of **Calla-lilies**, all included in the genus *Zantedeschia* and not in the genus *Calla* of which there is only one species [1002]. They are perennial rhizomatous plants from tropical and South Africa. The best known is the **Lily-of-the-Nile**, or **Arum Lily**, *Z. aethiopica* [1005], a robust plant up to 30 inches high with plain green, stalked, lanceolate leaves. The beautiful white spathe, up to 10 inches long, enfolds the base of the spadix and has a recurved margin. The male flowers occupy the upper part of the spadix and the female flowers are lower down. This is easily grown in wet conditions. There are several varieties which differ greatly in size.

1004
1005

1006
1007

Monstera deliciosa [1006] is a native of Mexico and Guatemala. It is a robust climber with stout stems and long-stalked leaves having ovate, perforated blades up to two feet across. It also produces hanging aerial roots, many of which never reach the ground. The cylindrical spadix is protected by a green, hooded spathe. The fruiting, cone-like spadix, covered with many small berries, is edible.

Spathiphyllum floribundum [1007] from Colombia has deep green, broadly lanceolate leaves and a stalked spadix with broad, pointed, white spathe.

Arisaema ringens [1008] from Japan has a tuber which produces two trilobed leaves about 18 inches long. The spadix is completely hidden by the green and white tubular spathe, which has a curved hood.

Lords-and-Ladies or **Cuckoo-pint**, *Arum maculatum* [1009], occurs in woods and other shady places throughout most of the British Isles, Europe and North Africa. It has a small underground tuber and the long-stalked leaves which appear in the spring have shiny, hastate blades up to eight inches long. In some plants the leaves are marked with dark blotches. Flowering occurs in April and May. The pale green spathe is up to 10 inches long and forms a cylindrical cavity with a narrow throat around the base of the spadix, with an open, hooded portion above. The upper, exposed part of the spadix is purple. Female flowers occur at the base of the spadix, and above these are sterile female flowers. Farther up is a band of male flowers and above these is a ring of sterile male flowers which form projecting filaments. The structure is attractive to small flies, which get trapped for a while and assist in cross-pollination. The fruit consists of scarlet berries.

1008
1009

The **Palm** family, *Palmae* or *Arecaceae* [1010-1017, 1019], includes at least 4,000 species of tropical or subtropical plants. They are woody shrubs or trees often with long, thick, unbranched stems and a crown of long-stalked, fan-shaped or pinnate leaves. The minute flowers are bisexual or unisexual and are borne in large, branched inflorescences. The fruit is more or less fleshy. The family is of great economic importance; it provides food, shelter and clothing for many peoples, and is the source of copra, coconuts, dates, rattan cane and raffia.

Borassus flabelliformis [1010] is a native of western tropical Africa but is widely cultivated; in India it is known as the **Palmyra Palm.** It is an unbranched tree attaining a height of 70 feet. The large leaves have spiny stalks and rounded, fan-like blades. The plants are unisexual and the small male flowers are borne on branched, catkin-like inflorescences. The female flowers occur on simpler spikes. The large brown fruit contains three hard seeds. Parts of this palm, including the hard black wood, are put to many uses. **Fortune's Palm,** *Trachycarpus excelsa* [1011], is widespread in Burma, China and Japan. It varies in height and may reach 40 feet in favourable conditions. It has fan-shaped leaves over two feet long and three feet wide, with long, toothed stalks. The minute, yellowish, unisexual flowers are borne in branched, pendulous clusters. The globose, bluish-black fruit is succulent. The fibrous remains of the leaves covering the trunk are used for making ropes and coarse fabric.

521

The **Double Coconut**, *Lodoicea maldivica*, is a palm from the Seychelles which reaches a height of 100 feet. The leaves have stalks from eight to 10 feet long and blades up to six feet across. The plants are unisexual. The fruit [1012] is a nut, containing a single seed, which may weigh up to 50 pounds. The seed takes 10 years to develop on the tree and about three years to germinate.

Calamus ciliaris [1013] is an India palm with pinnate leaves up to 30 inches long, each having from 80 to 100 hairy leaflets.

Chamaedorea ernesti-augusti [1014], from Colombia, has a thin, erect stem from three to four feet high and stalked, simple, dark green leaves about two feet long. The attractive, branched, flowering spikes are scarlet-orange.

1012
1013

1015

The **Oil Palm**, *Elaeis guineensis* [1015], from tropical west Africa has a thick trunk up to 30 feet high supported at the base by a mass of fibrous roots. It has dark green, pinnate leaves from 10 to 15 feet long. It is widely cultivated for the oil which is extracted from the fruits.

525

Rokhaya Sal.

1017

The **Coconut**, *Cocos nucifera* [1016, 1017], a native of the Cocos and Keeling Islands, is now widespread in the tropics where it is put to many uses. It is a slender palm up to 100 feet high with pinnate leaves from six to 20 feet long. The copious sap is used fresh or fermented to produce toddy, the fibrous outer layer of the fruit is coir, and the dried white flesh of the seed is used to make copra.

Licuala grandis [1019] is an attractive palm from the islands north of New Guinea. The leaves have long stalks and orbicular, fan-like blades.

The family *Cyclanthaceae* includes about 45 species of palm-like plants from the West Indies and tropical America. *Carludovica atrovirens* [1018] from Colombia has large, dark green leaves arising from the base of the plant. The small, unisexual flowers are borne in close, spirally arranged groups on a cylindrical spike enclosed in bracts. The dried leaves of *C. palmata* from Peru are cut into strips and used for making Panama hats.

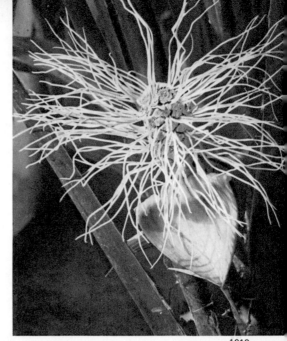

1018
1019

1020
1021

The **Water Plantain** family, *Alismataceae,* consists of about 80 species of aquatic herbs. Among them is the **Arrowhead,** *Sagittaria sagittifolia* [1020, 1021], widespread in shallow water at the margins of ponds and streams throughout north temperate regions of the Old World. It roots in the mud and produces some strap-shaped, submerged leaves, others with heart-shaped blades which lie on the surface of the water, and aerial leaves having long stalks and sagittate blades. The branched aerial inflorescences [1021] appear in July and August; the male flowers are at the top and the female flowers at the base. In North America its place is taken by *S. patifolia* and a number of other native species.

1022

The main genus in the **Pondweed** family, Potamogetonaceae, is *Potamogeton* with about 90 widespread species. *P. nodosus* [1022] occurs predominantly in the Mediterranean region and in central and western Europe but is also found in a few slow-flowing rivers in southern England. It has a creeping rhizome and submerged, broadly lanceolate, stalked leaves which are translucent and net-veined. The floating leaves are thicker and ovate. The dense cylindrical spikes of small, green, bisexual flowers appear above the water surface in August and September. Perennating winter buds (turions) are produced on slender stolons.

1023

The **Spiderwort** family, *Commelinaceae* [1023–1026], includes about 600 species of mainly tropical and subtropical herbs. They have alternate, entire leaves with parallel veins and bisexual flowers in various types of clusters. Each flower has three sepals, three petals and up to six stamens. The fruit is usually a capsule. The family is of no economic value, but some species are grown for ornament.

1024

1025

1026

Dichorisandra gaudichaudiana [1023] from Brazil has broad, lanceolate leaves from six to 10 inches long and a long cluster of blue and white flowers which appear in August.

Rhoeo discolor [1024] is a native of Mexico and the West Indies, and occurs in Florida. The lanceolate leaves are up to a foot long, striped above and dark purple below. The groups of small white flowers are surrounded by a compressed, cuplike bract in the axil of a leaf.

The **Common Spiderwort**, *Tradescantia virginiana* [1025], is a North American species up to three feet high with narrow leaves and white to deep purple flowers.

The **Wandering Jew**, *Zebrina pendula* [1026], from Mexico, with trailing, rooting stems and variegated leaves, is a commonly grown house plant, and occurs outdoors in Florida.

531

1027
1028

The important **Pineapple** family, *Bromeliaceae* [1027-1034, coloured plate XXXI], has about 2,000 species and is almost completely confined to tropical and warm temperate America. They are mostly short-stemmed plants with rosettes of thick spiny leaves. The flowers are usually bisexual and borne in a terminal inflorescence. The fruit is a berry or capsule. The family is important mainly for the edible pineapple; several species yield valuable fibres and a number are cultivated for ornament.

The **Pineapple**, *Ananas comosus* [1027, 1028, coloured plate XXXI], is a native of Brazil but is now cultivated in other tropical countries. It has a basal rosette of stiff, spiny, lanceolate leaves up to five feet long. The central, unbranched stem bears a cone-like inflorescence crowned by a tuft of small stiff leaves. The edible head [1028] is formed by the fleshy fruits and persistent bracts. There are numerous forms cultivated including those with variegated leaves. They do not set seed and are cultivated by suckers.

Cryptanthus zonatus [1029] from Brazil has a rosette of beautifully banded green and greyish leaves and a small, almost hidden central cluster of white flowers.

Aechmea fasciata [1030] from Brazil has a rosette of curved, oblong leaves marked with green and white bands. The pink flowers are subtended by pointed, rose-pink bracts and occur in a dense terminal head on an erect central stem. There is much confusion between this plant and the closely related *Billbergia* and in fact this species is sometimes known as *B. rhodocyanea*.

1031

1032

The genus *Billbergia* consists of about 40 species including *B. horrida* [1031] from Brazil. It has about 10 broad leaves up to 18 inches long with spiny margins which form a deep rosette. The central stem, about a foot long, bears a simple spike of green and violet flowers. Another Brazilian species, *B. nutans* [1032], is easily grown in a cool greenhouse. Each rosette has up to 15 narrow leaves about a foot long with a few marginal spines. The flowers are borne in drooping spikes about nine inches long. The bracts are pink and both the reddish sepals and yellow-green petals have blue margins.

1033

1034

Aechmea minuata [1033] from Brazil has leaves up to 18 inches long, and an erect red inflorescence of flowers with blue petals.

Tillandsia lindeniana [1034] from Peru has a rosette of long narrow leaves and a dense spike of flowers.

The family *Pontederiaceae* consists of about 28 species of tropical aquatic herbs. The best known is the **Water Hyacinth**, *Eichhornia crassipes* [1035], from South America. It floats freely in the water aided by the air sacs at the base of the leaf stalks.

The **Banana** family, *Musaceae*,
includes about 150 species of
large herbs widely distributed
in the tropics. They are sometimes tree-like in habit and
have large, alternate, entire or
pinnate leaves. The inflorescence is often a spike and the
flowers are bisexual or unisexual. The flower has six
unequal perianth parts, up to
six stamens and a three-celled
inferior ovary. The fruit is a
capsule or a berry. The economically important members
of the family belong to the
genus *Musa*, which includes
various species of **Bananas**
such as *M. sapientum* [1036,
1037]. This is a form from 20
to 30 feet high with oblong
leaves up to 10 feet long. The
inflorescence bears a number
of half-whorls of unisexual
flowers, male at the top and
female towards the base. The
male flowers are shed, and the
bunches of yellow curved
fruits develop on the then
pendulous inflorescence axis.
There are many cultivated
varieties of this banana, many
confined to particular regions.
Although given specific rank
here, it is probable that it
arose from the Indian species
M. paradisiaca, the **Plantain**
or **Adam's Fig.** This is also
widely cultivated in the tropics but the flesh is not so
sweet as that of the banana
and cannot be eaten raw.

1036

1

The family *Cannaceae* includes about 40 species of *Canna* spp., the best known being the **Indian Shot**, *C. indica* [1038], from the West Indies, which is often cultivated and has become naturalized from Florida to Texas. It is a coarse, erect perennial herb with simple, oblong leaves which range in colour from yellow to dark red. Although sepals and petals are present in the asymmetrical flower, the showy part consists of the six petaloid stamens, only one of which is fertile. The capsule contains many hard round seeds.

The **Arrowroot** family, *Marantaceae*, includes some 350 species of tropical and subtropical perennial herbs, which grow mostly in wet places. *Maranta bicolor* [1039] from Brazil is often grown for its attractive leaves which have basal sheaths, short stalks and ovate variegated blades. The small bisexual flower has only one fertile stamen, the other five being petaloid staminodes, or absent. The dehiscent fruit contains three seeds.

The **Ginger** family, *Zingiberaceae* [1040, coloured plate XXXII], includes about 1,400 tropical and subtropical rhizomatous herbs. The irregular bisexual flower has a showy, thin corolla and one fertile stamen with its filament more or less enveloping the slender style. The fruit is a capsule or a berry. Included in this family are *Zingiber ottensii* [1040] and *Hedychium gardnerianum* [coloured plate XXXII]. The latter is a native of northern India which reaches a height of six feet.

1038
1039

541

1041

1042

The **Grasses**, *Gramineae* [1041–1071], constitute one of the largest families of flowering plants with about 600 genera and probably 10,000 species. Although mainly herbaceous, they range from tiny annual herbs to the large woody bamboos. They may be densely tufted or have long creeping rhizomes. The erect stems are hollow and bear alternate leaves, each of which has a basal sheath surrounding the stem and a narrow, more or less elongated, blade. The minute flowers or florets are usually bisexual, and

in most grasses each has two swollen scales or lodicules, three stamens, and a central ovary with two feathery stigmas. In the bamboos each floret has six stamens. Each floret is generally enclosed between two scales, the lemma and palea, and these structures are borne in spikelets which are the basic unit of the grass inflorescence. The latter often has a complex structure; there may be from one to many florets in each spikelet. The flowers are wind pollinated and the one-seeded fruit or caryopsis is often

1043

1044

enclosed in the lemma and palea when shed.

The grasses are distributed throughout the world and in some parts constitute the dominant vegetation. They vary greatly in habit and occur in every type of habitat.

The family is also the most important one from the economic viewpoint. They provide forage for animals, grain and sugar for human consumption, and the raw materials for the production of saki, whisky and rum; and have many other uses. They are the basis of our lawns and playing fields and a large number are grown as ornamental plants.

The fruits of **Wheat**, *Triticum aestivum* [1041], are shed without the lemma and palea; the position of the small, shield-shaped embryo can be seen at one side towards the base of the grain. The fruits of **Rye**, *Secale cereale* [1042], are also naked but those of the **Long-eared Barley**, *Hordeum distichon* [1043], and **Oats**, *Avena sativa* [1044], are tightly enclosed between the lemma and palea.

1045

1046

The **Common Reed**, *Phragmites communis* [1045], occurs in swamps and shallow water throughout most regions of the world. It is a stout, perennial, rhizomatous grass with stiff, erect stems from four to nine feet high. The leaves have loose sheaths and flat, pointed blades. The lax, purplish inflorescences, from six to 12 inches long, appear in August and September. The small spikelets have from three to six flowers, and the grain is enclosed in the thick lemma and palea. Its dense network of rhizomes and roots help to prevent erosion of lake and river margins and the dried stems are used for thatching.

Rice, *Oryza sativa* [1046], is one of the most important food crops and it is estimated that at least half the world's population subsists wholly or partially on the grain. Most of it is grown and eaten in India, China and Japan. It has been cultivated in these countries for hundreds of years and there are many different strains but it is doubtful whether the species exists today in the wild state. More recently fairly extensive cultivation has been undertaken in the southern United States and the Northern Territory of Australia. It is an erect annual grass with loose inflorescences of one-flowered spikelets. Methods of cultivation vary but usually during the period of vegetative growth the paddy fields are flooded. The water is drained off to facilitate harvesting.

The **Barleys** belong to the genus *Hordeum*, of which there are about 20 species. It is one of the oldest of cultivated cereals, and there is clear evidence that it was grown and eaten in Egypt and China over 4,500 years ago. It was formerly used for making bread but now it is grown mainly for animal feed and malt for the brewing industry. The cultivated barleys are annual plants with condensed spike-like inflorescences. The one-flowered spikelets are in groups of three, the groups forming two opposite vertical rows along the main axis. The lemmas and the glumes at the base of spikelets usually have long bristly awns.

In the **Two-row Barley**, *H. distichon* [1047], the lateral spikelets are more or less aborted so that the mature ear bears only two vertical rows of grains. In the **Six-row Barley**, *H. vulgare* [1048], all the spikelets are fertile, with the result that there are six vertical rows of grains in the mature ear. These two species are grown mostly in the north temperate zone and annual world production exceeds 50 million tons.

1047

1048

545

The **Wall Barley**, *H. murinum* [1049], occurs throughout much of the north temperate zone. It is a coarse annual from eight to 24 inches high found growing in waste places, particularly near the sea. It has more or less erect stems and flat, slightly hairy leaf blades. The terminal, awned spikes are up to four inches long and appear in June and July. The lateral spikelets in each group are male or sterile, and it is only the medium one that produces a grain. When mature, the group of the spikelets with the single grain is shed as a unit.

The **Fox-tail Barley**, *H. jubatum* [1050], is a native of North America. It is a perennial with long silky awns spreading from the small spikelets.

1049
1050

Rye, *Secale cereale* [1051], is unknown as a wild species although it commonly occurs as a naturalized escape from cultivation. It can tolerate cool climates and poor soils more readily than most cereals, and is an important crop in northern Europe and western Asia. It is still used for bread-making, but the bulk provides an important animal feed. It is also used for hay-making and the long straw is valuable for thatching. It is the basis of American whisky.

Under cultivation rye is an annual with a well-developed root system and erect, slender, purplish stems. The inflorescence is a dense terminal spike of awned, three-flowered spikelets. The uppermost floret is abortive so that only two grains are produced in each spikelet.

The cultivated rye has originated from either *S. montanum*, a native of the Mediterranean region, or *S. anatolicum*, found in south-west Asia. As no evidence of rye has been found in Egyptian ruins it is believed that it is of more recent origin than barley or wheat.

As in other cereals the grain is liable to germinate if the ears are beaten down by heavy rain [1052].

1051
1052

1053
1054

It is known that **Wheat** was grown in the Nile Valley in 5000 B.C. and in England 3,000 years later. The origin of our modern wheats is complex and probably involved natural hybridization between members of the genus *Triticum* and species of *Agropyron* and *Aegilops*. The main bread-wheat cultivated today is *T. aestivum* (= *T. vulgare* = *T. sativum*) [1053, 1054]. It is unknown in the wild state and its origin is obscure but it probably arose during the Iron Age, about 1000 B.C. There are many varieties in cultivation and new ones with desirable features such as short stems, large ears, resistance to disease, are continually being produced. It is an annual with a fibrous root system and several erect shoots. The inflorescence is a terminal spike with two rows of laterally compressed spikelets each containing from one to six florets. In some varieties [1054] long awns are present.

The **Club Wheat**, *T. compactum* [1055], probably had an origin similar to that of the bread-wheat. It is grown mostly in Chile, the western United States, and India.

One of the ancestors of some of our modern wheats was undoubtedly the **Einkorn Wheat**, *T. monococcum*. This produces only one grain per spikelet and the yield is low but it grows in poor, rocky ground and is still cultivated in mountain regions of southern Europe. It must be one of the earliest cultivated plants, for it has been found on the site of Swiss lake dwellings of the Stone Age. The **Emmer** wheat, *T. dicoccum*, was also in cultivation during the same period and is still occasionally grown in the mountains of Europe.

World production of wheat is in the region of 150 million tons per year. Originating in the Old World, wheat is now grown in many other regions. It was introduced into Mexico by the Spaniards in 1520, and today the United States and Canada, together with Argentina and Australia, are the main wheat exporting countries.

There are about 10 wild species of **Oats**, *Avena* spp., in temperate regions but the **Cultivated Oat**, *A. sativa* [1056], is not known in the wild state. It probably arose from *A. fatua*, the **Wild Oat**, a native of Europe and Asia. It is an erect annual grass with a loose terminal inflorescence. Each slender branch of the inflorescence terminates in a large pendulous spikelet of from one to seven florets. The uppermost florets are often male or sterile, and the lemmas may or may not be awned. Annual world production of oats is about 65 million tons, mostly from temperate Europe and North America. It can withstand a wider range of soils and climate than most cereals and has apparently been in cultivation since 2500 B.C.

1057
1058

The genus *Stipa* includes about 100 species of perennial grasses which are widespread but particularly characteristic of savannas and steppes. They have narrow leaves and one-flowered spikelets. The long-awned, sharp-pointed fruits of some species can seriously injure sheep by penetrating the skin. *S. joannis* [1057] grows in central Europe and on mountains in the Mediterranean region. The feathery awns are up to a foot long. Other members of the genus are *S. tenacissima*, **Esparto Grass**, from Spain and North Africa, with short feathery awns, and the **Porcupine-grass**, *S. spartea*, a native of the United States from Illinois to California with a strongly twisted awn six inches long.

1059

1060

Timothy, *Phleum pratense* [1058], is a native of north, western and central Europe and in wet meadows of England and Wales. It is a valuable hay grass which is commonly cultivated in most temperate countries. It is an erect perennial from one to four feet high with rough, greyish-green leaves. The narrow, terminal inflorescence is up to nine inches long and appears in July. The crowded, compressed spikelets each contain a single floret. It is a hardy, shallow-rooting grass and a large number of strains have been produced. *P. bertolonii* is a similar species which occurs in old grassland and shallow downs.

The **Meadow Foxtail**, *Alopecurus pratensis* [1059], is found throughout most of the British Isles, Europe, the Caucasus, northern Asia and North America. It is an erect perennial grass from one to three feet high

with rough leaf blades. The dense terminal tapering inflorescences are two or three inches long and appear between April and June. The compressed spikelet contains a single floret which does not have a palea. This grass is common on heavy soils and selected strains are valuable for hay and grazing when mixed with other species.

Hare's-tail, *Lagurus ovatus* [1060], is a native of the Mediterranean which has become widely naturalized in southern England, Australia, South Africa and South America. It is a hairy annual from two to 24 inches high with greyish-green leaves. The soft, woolly, ovoid inflorescences are produced between June and August. The compressed spikelet contains a single floret. This beautiful grass is often grown for the attractive flowering heads.

1061

The genus *Sesleria* includes 10 species native in
Europe and western Asia. They are tufted perennial
grasses with ovoid spike and compressed spikelets
containing few florets. *S. uliginosa* [1061] occurs in
fens in northern and eastern Europe. *S. albicans*
[1062], the **Blue Moor-grass**, occurs in central and
south-west Europe and is common on calcareous
hill pastures in northern England and western

Ireland. It is a wiry grass from six to 18 inches high with flat, glaucous leaf blades. The bluish-grey, shiny, ovoid spikes are less than an inch long and appear in April and May. The spikelet contains two or three florets and the grain is enclosed within the lemma and palea.

1063

Koeleria glauca [1063] grows in non-alkaline, usually sandy soils in central Europe and western Asia. It is an erect perennial grass up to 18 inches high with small, grey-green leaves. The narrow, shiny inflorescence, which appears between April and July, has compressed spikelets each containing two or three florets. *K. cristata* is distributed over wide areas of the United States.

The **Rye-grass**, *Lolium perenne* [1064], not to be confused with **Rye** (p. 547), is a native of Europe and Asia which has been introduced into North America and Australia. It is a perennial from one to two feet high with smooth stems and leaves. The elongated inflorescence appears between May and August. It has alternate, distant spikelets which are edgewise on to the main axis. Each spikelet has from eight to 11 florets. This is a very variable species and hybrids with the **Meadow-grass**, *Festuca pratensis*, are fairly common.

Couch-grass or **Twitch**, *Agropyron repens* [1065], is a widespread and persistent weed through the north temperate zone. It has a creeping rhizome and erect stems from one to three feet high. The spikelets have from three to five florets each and are inserted laterally on the inflorescence.

1064

1065

Cock's-foot or **Orchard Grass**, *Dactylis glomerata* [1066], is widespread in Europe, Asia, North America and North Africa. It has been introduced into other temperate areas and some strains are very useful for pasture or hay. It is a coarse, tufted perennial up to three feet high with rough, flat leaves. The inflorescence, with its dense groups of flattened two- to five-flowered spikelets, appears between May and August.

The **Broom-corn** or **Proso Millet**, *Panicum miliaceum* [1067], may be the millet of the ancient Swiss Lake dwellers and may have been in cultivation before wheat. It is an annual from three to four feet high with soft leaves and large, loose, drooping inflorescences. Today it is extensively grown in Russia and Central Asia and the grain enclosed in the hard, shiny lemma and palea is fed to cage-birds.

1066

1067

1069

1070

The **Giant Bamboo**, *Dendrocalamus giganteus* [1068], from Java is one of the largest grasses and may reach 100 feet in height.

Maize, Indian Corn or, in America, **Corn**, *Zea mays* [1069–1071], is very different from any other known plant. It is unknown in the wild and its origin is obscure; it may have come from the Andes region of north-west South America. It is a coarse, erect annual with prop-roots and large leaves. The male flowers are produced in a branched terminal inflorescence, the tassel, and the female flowers are borne on a short axillary axis protected by large bracts. The female flowers have very long stigmas, the silks, which project in a group between the tips of the bracts. The maize cob consists of the axis with the fruits attached. There are several kinds: popcorn, which bursts when heated; flint corn, with hard grains; flour corn, with soft grains; sweet corn, which is sugary; and the highly productive dent corn, which has a hard grain with a soft patch. Most of the maize grown is fed to stock; much is eaten by man, and it yields Bourbon whisky, various oils, syrups and building materials. World production is now about 200 million tons per year.

INDEX

A

Abies, 73–75
  A. alba, 73
  A. concolor, 74
  A. procera, 74
Abutilon darwinii, 312
  A. hybridum, 312
  A. striatum, 312
Acacia, 222–223
  False, 226
  Senegal, 223
Acalypha hispida, 314
Acantholimon venustum, 164
Acanthus, 434–435
  A. mollis, 434; var. niger, 434–435
  A. spinosus, 435
Acer, 367
  A. negundo, 369
  A. plantanoides, 368
  A. pseudoplatanus, 367, 368
Aceraceae, 367
Achillea millefolium, 277
  A. schurii, 278
Achimenes erecta, 438
Achras sapota, 247
Acocanthera spectabilis, 348
Aconite, Winter, 115
Aconitum, 119
  A. vulparia, 119
Acorus calamus, 514
Actinomyces griseus, 11
Actinomycetales, 11
Actinoptychus adriaticus, 17
Adam's Fig, 538
Adansonia digitata, 308
Adonis aestivalis, 120, 122
  A. vernalis, 122
Aechmea fasciata, 534
  A. minuata, 536
Aegilops, 548
Aesculus, 370
  A. carnea, 371
  A. hippocastanum, 370
  A. pavia, 371
African Lily, 452
African Marigold, 277
African Violet, 437
Agapanthus, 452
  A. umbellatus, 452
Agaric, Fly, 38
Agaricaceae, 36
Agaricus arvensis, 36
  A. augustus, 37

Agave filifera, 480
  A. sisalana, 480
Agave Cactus, 148
Agrimony, Hemp, 265
Agropyron, 548
  A. repens, 555
Agrostemma githago, 160
Ailanthus altissima, 331
Aizoaceae, 156
Ajuga reptans, 407
Alchemilla vulgaris, 206
Alder, 171
  Green, 171
Alfalfa, 231
Alfileria, 326
Algae, 12–25, 45
  Blue-green, 13
  Brown, 23–25
  Green, 22–23
  Red, 23
Alismataceae, 528
Alliaria officinalis, 138
  A. petiolata, 138
Allium, 454
  A. karataviense, 455
  A. montanum var. petraeum, 455
  A. paradoxum, 456
  A. schoenoprasum, 454
  A. victorialis, 455
Allspice, Carolina, 189
Almond, Dwarf Russian, 213
Alnus glutinosa, 171
  A. viridis, 171
Aloe, 452
  Partridge-breasted, 452
Aloe aristata, 452
  A. variegata, 452
Alopecurus pratensis, 551
Alpenrose, 235
Alpine Auricula, 141
Alpine Crowfoot, 127
Alpine Strawberry, 205
Althaea officinalis, 313
  A. rosea, 313
Alyssum, Golden, 139
Alyssum saxatile, 139
Amanita muscaria, 38
  A. vaginata, 40
Amaranthaceae, 165
Amaranthus caudatus, 165
Amaryllidaceae, 474–480
Amazon Lily, 478
Amelanchier laevis, 221
American Arbor-vitae, 90

D

Dactylis glomerata, 556
Dactylorchis, 496–497
    D. fuchsii, 496
    D. sambucina, 497
Daedalacanthus nervosus, 435
Daedalea confragosa, 33
Daffodil, Wild, 479
Daisy, 267
    Barberton or Transvaal, 300
    Moon, 279
    Ox-eye, 297
Dahlia, 274
    Cactus, 275
    Garden, 274–275
Dahlia rosea, 275
    D. juarezii, 275
Dalechampia roezliana, 315
Danewort, 388
Daphne arbuscula, 356
    D. mezereum, 356
Date, 521
Datura stramonium, 418
Daucus carota, 385; subsp. sativus, 385
Davidia involucrata, 373
Dawn-redwood, 88
Day-lily, 450
Deadly Nightshade, 417
Deadnettle, Red, 409
    White, 409
Delosperma echinatum, 156
Delphinium oxysepalum, 117
Dendrobium, 502–503
    D. nobile, 502
    D. phalaenopsis var. schroederianum, 504
Dendrocalamus giganteus, 557
Dendrochilum, 502
    D. glumaceum, 502
Deodar, 80
Desmid, 22
Deutzia scabra, 191
Dianthus, 163
    D. barbatus, 163
    D. glacialis, 163
    D. praecox, 163
    D. superbus, 163
Diatoms, 17–21
Dicentra spectabilis, 132
Dichorisandra gaudichaudiana, 531
Dicranum polysetum, 53
Dictamnus albus, 329
Dieffenbachia picta, 517
Digitalis, 428

D. ferruginea, 428
D. grandiflora, 428
D. purpurea, 428
Dill, 381
Dioon edule, 98
Diploneis crabro, 18
Dipsacaceae, 394
Dipsacus fullonum, 394
Dock, 166
Dodder, Large, 396
Dodecatheon meadia, 142
Dog Rose, 206, 209
Dog-hobble, 239
Dog's-tooth Violet, 456
Dogwood, 374–378
    Flowering, 377
Dombeya wallichii, 308
Doronicum austriacum, 284
    D. clusii, 284
    D. cordatum, 286
Dorstenia, 183
    D. radiata, 183
Double Coconut, 522
Douglas Fir, 75
    Colorado, 75
    Large-coned, 75
Draba aizoides, 137
Dracaena, 471
    D. draco, 471
    D. fragrans, 471
Dragon Tree, 471
Drosera, 199
    D. rotundifolia, 199
Droseraceae, 199
Dryas octopetala, 205
Dryopteris felix-mas, 69
Durmast Oak, 177
Dwarf Russian Almond, 213
Dyer's Rocket, 133

E

Earth-ball, 42
Earth-star, 41
Eastern Hemlock, 75
Ecballium elaterium, 255
Echeveria setosa, 196
Echinocactus eyriesii, 149
Echinops sphaerocephalus, 290
Echium vulgare, 404
Edelweiss, 270
Egyptian Cotton, 311
Egyptian Lotus Flower, 109

S

Saccharomyces fragilis, 26
Sacred Lotus, 109
Saffron, Meadow, 446
Sage Brush, 283
Sagittaria sagittifolia, 528
  S. patifolia, 528
St Bruno's Lily, 446
Saintpaulia ionantha, 437
  S. kewensis, 437
Salicaceae, 248–249
Salicornia herbacea, 164
Salix, 248–249
  S. alba var. coerulea, 249; var. vitellina, 249
  S. reticulata, 249
Salvia sclarea, 410
Salvinia natans, 71
Salviniales, 71
Sambucus ebulus, 388
  S. nigra, 387
Sansevieria trifasciata, 471
Santolina caespitosa, 278
Sapindaceae, 369
Sapodilla Plum, 247
Sapotaceae, 247
Sarothamnus scoparius, 225; subsp. maritimus
    225
Sarracenia purpurea, 132
Sarraceniaceae, 104, 132
Sauce-alone, 138
Saussurea alpina, 298
Savin, 94
Saxifraga assimilis, 198
  S. paniculata, 198
Saxifragaceae, 190, 192, 197–198, 205–206
Saxifrage, 197–198, 205–206
Scabiosa ochroleuca, 394
Scabious, 394
Scenedesmus quadricauda, 22
Scentless Mayweed, 279
Schizomycetes, 9
Scilla bifolia, 463
Scirpus maritimus, 491
Scleroderma aurantium, 42
  S. verrucosum, 42
Scolymus hispanicus, 302
Scopolia carniolica, 420
Scotch Thistle, 295
Scots Pine, 83
Scrophularia nodosa, 426
  S. vernalis, 426
Scrophulariaceae, 423–431
Scutellaria pinnatifida, 407

Sea Buckthorn, 356
Sea Holly, 383
Sea Island Cotton, 311
Sea Lavender, 164
Sea Pink, 164
Secale anatolicum, 547
  S. cereale, 543, 547
  S. montanum, 547
Sedge, 487
Sedum hispanicum, 196
Selaginella kraussiana, 56
  S. selaginoides, 56
Self-heal, 407
Sempervivum montanum, 194
Senecio, 286–288
  S. crassissimus, 288
  S. cruentus, 286
  S. cuneatus, 288
  S. sibiricus, 288
  S. vernalis, 286
Senna, Bladder, 228
Sequoiadendron giganteum, 86
Servian Spruce, 78
Service Tree, Wild, 221
Sesleria albicans, 552
  S. uliginosa, 552
Sessile Oak, 177
Seville Orange, 331
Shaggy Cap, 37
Shellbark Hickory, 170
Shepherd's Purse, 136
Shinleaf, 234
Shooting-star, 142
Shrubby Cinquefoil, 203
Silene acaulis, 162
  S. alba, 162
  S. dioica, 162
Silk-cotton Tree, 308
Silkgrass, 469
Silver Bell Tree, 247
Silver Birch, 171
Silver Fir, European, 73
Silverweed, 204
Silybum marianum, 298
Simaroubaceae, 331
Sinningia speciosa, 438
Six-row Barley, 545
Skimmia, Japanese, 330
Skimmia japonica, 330
Skullcap, 407
Skunk-cabbage, 516
Slime Mould, 26
Sloe, 212
Small Bur-parsley, 383

PICTURE ACKNOWLEDGEMENTS

Ing. F. Benčat; Č. Böhm; K. Celba; Crown copyright: reproduced with the permission of Her Majesty's Stationery Office and of the Director, The Royal Botanic Gardens, Kew; J. E. Downward; J. Fiala; Prof. Dr B. Fott; R. H. Hall; Dr A. Z. Hnízdo; Dr M. Hostička; Ing. J. Jeník; Dr K. Jirák; Dr V. Jirásek; Dr S. Kaufman; Dr I. Klášterský; Ing. Z. Kříž; Prof. Dr J. Kunský; G. Lauckner; Dr V. Michal; Dr J. Mikeš; The Natural History Photographic Agency; Dr M. Nermut; Prof. Dr F. A. Novák; Dr A. Pilát; Prof. Dr S. Prát; Dr M. C. F. Proctor; A. Pustka; roebild; J. Rubín; Dr J. Seget; Dr V. J. Staněk; Dr J. Stárka; Ing. I. Svoboda; Ing. Dr K. Šmirous; R. Šubík; Dr F. Táborský; John Topham Ltd; Dr J. Tříska; Ing. Dr Z. Vulterin; Dr Paul Wolff & Tritschler.